GROWING
UP IN THE
GRASSROOTS

GROWING UP IN THE GRASSROOTS

FINDING UNITY IN CLIMATE ACTIVISM ACROSS GENERATIONS

JOY REEVES

NEW DEGREE PRESS

GROWING UP IN THE GRASSROOTS

Finding Unity in Climate Activism Across Generations

ISBN   978-1-64137-948-9   *Paperback*

978-1-64137-989-2   *Kindle Ebook*

978-1-64137-760-7   *Ebook*

For Dad—thank you for helping me grow. You are my example.

CONTENTS

———

INTRODUCTION

"Okay, boomer."

Two simple words, and the movement was launched. One dismissive little hashtag, and the Internet hosted the intergenerational feud defining the 2010s, printing it on t-shirts, surfacing at climate conferences and social justice demonstrations across the nation, pitting postmodern "snowflakes" against backward "boomers." Because the U.S. isn't polarized enough, right?

The exact origins of "okay, boomer" are uncertain, tracing back to a 2009 post buried somewhere in the abyss of Reddit. Ten years later, teens repopularized the phrase on the video sharing platform TikTok, where it quickly went viral. Its meaning? *Your views are so outdated, I am not going to take the time to re-explain these issues to you.*

The video that actually prompted the revival of "okay, boomer" was a digital rant posted by a white-haired man in a baseball cap. "The millennials and Generation Z have the Peter Pan syndrome," he declared, grinning into his selfie camera.

"They don't ever want to grow up!" (The man seemed well aware of his audience: over 60 percent of TikTok's monthly active users in the U.S. are ten to twenty-four-year-olds.)[1] In response, a Gen Z user posted a reaction video saying, "Okay, boomer," and adding, "Have a terrible day."

Thousands of fed-up young users rallied in her stead in a mash-up of videos, memes, rap music, art, and reactions to other cringeworthy internet content posted by older users, employing the same phrase and same sentiment. It has been called "the digital equivalent of an eye roll" by *The New York Times.*[2]

And, yes, it has already made it into online dictionaries:[3]

Okay, boomer [oh-key boom-er]

"Okay, boomer" is a viral internet slang phrase used, often in a humorous or ironic manner, to call out or dismiss out-of-touch or close-minded opinions associated with the baby boomer generation and older people more generally.

While many young people either laugh at or rally behind the phrase, it is frankly hard for me to do either. As a student in scientific communication, I am trained every day to find

---

1   "20 TikTok Stats for Marketers: TikTok Demographics, Statistics, & Key Data," Mediakix.

2   Taylor Lorenz, "'OK Boomer' Marks the End of Friendly Generational Relations," *The New York Times*, October 29, 2019.

3   *Dictionary.com*, Slang ed. s.v., "OK Boomer."

common ground between conflicting interests, combine science and economic policy to negotiate win-win scenarios, and take the time to understand all perspectives. I can't help but equate "okay, boomer" to *giving up* on those ideals, in a sense, let alone an outright insult. The fact that many videos are punctuated by "have a terrible day" confirms the dismissive negativity I suspected from the beginning.

For fear of being called a complete Loyalist, I would add the disclaimer that ageism and stereotyping come from both sides. I completely understand the frustration Gen Zers and millennials are expressing toward the outdated views of a few individual boomers (particularly with regard to social and racial justice). However, what I disagree with is the generalized assumption that anyone over the age of forty "just doesn't get it."

In my field, environmental science and policy, the vast majority of climate data, federal environmental agencies, and lifesaving pollution regulation systems were spearheaded by older generations. In fact, it was my parents' generation who originally took to the streets on the first Earth Day in 1970 and throughout the decade, oddly reminiscent of the student climate marches my friends and I attend today at the same adolescent age.

In the context of climate, there's no doubt the situation demands urgency. Though older and younger generations alike are frustrated—and perhaps step out of line occasionally with that frustration through personal attacks over the internet—today's problem lies in chalking up this conflict to a *given*. "Okay, boomer" assumes both "sides" are completely inflexible in their views on climate change. Through the journey of this book, I have found this is simply not true.

This book will delve into the most powerful commonalities between Americans old and young, conservative and liberal, urban and rural. These are the commonalities that inspired monumental environmental progress in the 1970s and persist today:

- Caring for the future of children
- Wanting to create jobs
- Striving to minimize human suffering
- Practicing the religious concept of stewardship
- Playing outside as a kid
- Enjoying a walk in the woods
- Having a love for animals
- Cherishing the national parks that make us proud Americans
- Safeguarding our individual rights to clean air and clean water

By recognizing these common values and crafting a message that tactfully intertwines them with climate action, this book will show you what it means to be a true communicator, and most importantly, a twenty-first century environmental activist.

A visualization...

I want you to imagine you're old. A great-grandparent. You're sitting in an armchair, enjoying your morning coffee and virtual reality gaming session or whatever, when your great-grandkids come scampering up to you and ask you to explain an unfamiliar image in their textbook of something only your generation remembers.

So, you hit 'em with the "back in my day…," but instead of talking about a record player or a VCR tape, you are talking about the Outer Banks. Or the Great Barrier Reef you once snorkeled in. Or seeing a black bear for the first time in your favorite state park. The possibility that our grandchildren will not be able to relate to some of these experiences in nature, the "Once Was" phenomenon, as I call it, is beyond sobering.

The "Once Was" phenomenon, meaning that my current generation will experience a greener, safer, and more diversely inhabited world than the one my grandchildren will experience, is an argument that will always resonate in the grassroots.

Sure, there's also the practical price tag argument—in the past decade, we've already spent about 1.4 trillion dollars fixing damage from climate-related disasters.[4] And that monetary cost is only going to increase—but the non-monetary costs are what keep me up at night: the already-increasing loss of human lives to drought and disasters across the world, the loss of millions of years of evolution as a single species goes extinct, and the dulling of a panoramic

---

4   Adam B. Smith, "2017 U.S. Billion-Dollar Weather and Climate Disasters: A Historic Year in Context," NOAA: Beyond the Data, January 8, 2018.

landscape from a wash of green to the blurred greyscale of industrial development.

The "Once Was" is why I personally care about climate change.

I worked in a lab this past summer studying saltwater intrusion on the coast of North Carolina, which gave me an unexpected glimpse into the tangible progression of sea level rise.

One day, my lab took a day trip to the Alligator River National Wildlife Refuge, which sat directly on the coastline of North Carolina. Toward the end of our three-hour drive, I looked out the window and noticed something I'd never really picked up on before: a large swath of dead trees, protruding out of water and marsh like skeletal toothpicks, completely stripped of their healthy branches. I learned these are called "ghost forests," and they're the product of severe landscape change. Droughts, storms, and rising sea levels cause salty oceanwater to be pushed inland through agricultural drainage canals, essentially poisoning forests through their soils.

Ghost forests are actually all over the eastern coasts of the United States (and the world), next to roads, waterways, and even inland fields, sometimes stretching on for miles. The National Oceanic and Atmospheric Administration (NOAA) eerily defines a ghost forest as "the watery remains of a once-verdant woodland."[5] Sometimes

5   NOAA, "What is a Ghost Forest?" National Ocean Service website, last modified April 9, 2020.

half-submerged and with fairly dismal chances of recovering to their healthier and more beautiful state, ghost forests serve as visual reminders of the "Once Was" phenomenon. I could see it in the eyes of the refuge managers we talked to—parts of their treasured refuge were going to be lost.

I certainly didn't want to sound like an overdramatic intern at the time, but it felt like I was witnessing climate change. And that stuck with me.

However, as depressing as the "Once Was" tends to be, I find it equally empowering to come to terms with the "Once Was" and surge ahead toward the "What's Next?"

I wrote this book because it is my peace offering—my personal contribution to the widespread, exasperated push for unity we're seeing in the divided United States right now. There's nothing more inspiring to me than working alongside people who devote their lives to an environmental field on the front lines of either science or activism—whether it be the mentorship of my lab supervisors and PIs over that summer, the support of my professors at Duke, or the example of my dad, who has been an environmentalist his entire life. It was he who inspired me to go into the field itself, my first hint that my generation shouldn't take this on alone.

I think it's more than possible to cross generational divides in climate activism—it's essential. I loosely define "activism" in such a way that everyone can participate. It could mean rallying in the streets, actively pursuing scientific research, teaching and educating others, or having a one-on-one conversation. And the meaning of "grassroots" is rather simple: it starts with people, bottom-up. My hope is that, in reading this book, you will discover there are vast opportunities for older and younger generations to find common ground and room for mentorship to move forward collaboratively on climate change.

One aspect of climate change people are arguing about less and less is the scientific data underlying it. The best places to look for scientific data are the Intergovernmental Panel on Climate Change (IPCC), the National Academies of Science, and the NOAA. In fact, because these resources are so readily accessible, I'm going to keep the core "science" of this book rather limited. But in short, economic and population growth through the pre-industrial era have caused anthropogenic greenhouse gas emissions to rise higher than ever. Throughout the past 800,000 years, the atmospheric concentrations of carbon dioxide, methane, and nitrous oxide have never been higher than they are today.[6] Their widespread effects are "extremely likely" to have caused warming since the mid-1900s, leading over 97 percent of scientists to come to the consensus that human-caused greenhouse gas emissions are warming the planet.[7]

---

6   Rebecca Lindsey, "Climate Change: Atmospheric Carbon Dioxide," NOAA Climate.gov, February 20, 2020.

7   John Cook et al., "Consensus on Consensus: A Synthesis of Consensus Estimate on Human-Caused Global Warming," *Environmental Research Letters* 11, no. 4 (April 2016): 1.

But the current event you've probably heard the most about in national news is the alarming conclusion of the IPCC's 2018 Special Report declaring that any warming beyond 2°C could put us at a critical level of no return.[8] And, right now, we're on track to easily hit that point. The future of humanity is in jeopardy, and the report gives us only about ten years to get it right (requiring a scale of action "for which there is no documented historical precedent," a bit of a scary phrase coming from the IPCC).[9] So, how do we mobilize nations in a single decade?

One of the best ways is to show people—and politicians—that climate change is happening *now*, and its effects resonate far beyond the district limits of Washington or the borders of the United States. I take pride in the economic resilience of our country, but we can't treat a climate catastrophe like a recession. Ice melts, coastlines disappear, ecosystems die. Communities suffer and scatter. Climate change is the wickedest of wicked problems, characteristically woven from chain reactions and positive feedback loops, meaning our continued "procrastination" in implementing sweeping policy changes may leave no chance for bounce-back.

Scientists have boiled down the irreversible nature of climate change into eight worldwide "tipping points" from which

---

8   IPCC, Special Report: Global Warming of 1.5°C, Summary for Policy-
    makers (IPCC, 2018), 5.

9   IPCC, Special Report: Global Warming of 1.5°C (IPCC, 2018), C.2.1.

there is no return.[10] Many of them will be triggered by as little as 2°C warming.

THE BIG PICTURE TIPPING POINTS:

1. **Amazon rainforest:** Frequent droughts, an 80 percent increase[11] in fires from 2018-2019 (many of which could be viewed from space), and continued deforestation; 17 percent has been lost to deforestation since 1970.

2. **Arctic sea ice:** Loss of area, September sea ice declining at a rate of 12.85 percent per decade relative to 1981-2010 period.[12]

3. **Circulation of the Atlantic Ocean:** Observed slowdown since the 1950s, interconnected to many of these other tipping points.

4. **Boreal forest:** Changes to fire regimes, dieback in forests, and permafrost thaw.

5. **Coral reefs:** Large-scale die-offs and mass coral bleaching; studies estimate half of the Great Barrier Reef has been bleached to death since 2016.[13] With a 2°C increase

---

10 Timothy M. Lenton et al., "Climate Tipping Points—Too Risky to Bet Against," *Nature* 575, no. 7784 (November 2019): 592–95

11 Sarah Gibbens, "The Amazon Is Burning at Record Rates—and Deforestation is to Blame," *National Geographic*, August 21, 2019

12 "Arctic Sea Ice Minimum," Jet Propulsion Laboratory, NASA, accessed April 10, 2020.

13 Lauren E. James, "Half of the Great Barrier Reef Is Dead," *National Geographic*, August 2018.

in global average temperatures, we could lose 99 percent of tropical corals.[14]

6. **Greenland ice sheet:** Ice melting at an accelerating rate—a total loss would account for 7m of sea level rise in the long term.[15]

7. **Permafrost:** Thawing globally to release carbon dioxide and methane and further exacerbate warming.

8. **Antarctica:** Loss of ice accelerating; instability of Western and Eastern ice sheets.

Looking at these tipping points factually negates the belief once held by over half of Americans that "climate change won't affect me personally." However, despite an abundance of scientific data, a climate consciousness age gap persists. Seventy percent of Americans ages eighteen to thirty-four are worried a great deal or fair amount about climate change compared to only 56 percent of Americans ages fifty-five and older, according to a 2018 Gallup Poll.[16] As high of a percentage as 70 percent may be, it has been argued that what adolescents may have in passion and social media-propagated concern, they lack in money, legislative influence, and political power. That is, until a fifteen-year-old girl named Greta Thunberg (and legions of activists standing behind her) took the podium.

---

14 IPCC, Special Report on 1.5°C, Summary for Policymakers, 8.

15 M. Tedesco et al., "Greenland Ice Sheet," NOAA Arctic Program, accessed January 2, 2020.

16 RJ Reinhart, "Global Warming Age Gap: Younger Americans Most Worried," Gallup Poll News Release, May 11, 2018.

Right now, Greta Thunberg is a household name. Her heart-wrenching call to action that launched it all for "Generation Greta" went something like this:

This is all wrong. I shouldn't be up here. I should be back in school on the other side of the ocean. Yet you all come to us young people for hope. How dare you. You have stolen my dreams and my childhood with your empty words. [...] You are failing us. But the young people are starting to understand your betrayal. The eyes of all future generations are upon you. And if you choose to fail us, I say: We will never forgive you.[17]

Thunberg's words have now traveled far beyond the 2019 UN Climate Action Summit. And she refuses to step back from her position.

She even turned down a meeting with President Donald Trump, explaining that "it would be a waste of time, really."

Reactions to her rallying cry are mixed; some worship her as a figurehead of the New Environmental Movement, while others fear or condemn the cold anger she expresses. Part of the reason for this divide is that current environmental protests tend to come across as a bit of an "F-U" from my

---

17 *United Nations,* "Climate Action Summit 2019—Morning Session," September 23, 2019, video, 41:00.

generation (for lack of a more polite term). The sentiment surrounding the movement seems to blame older generations, when in reality, older environmentalists have been some of the most fervent fighters in today's movement—even when eclipsed by younger faces. Talking to activists of all ages throughout this book, I've learned that environmental movements come from a place of passion, and underlying common values, more than from a place of anger. So, no matter how angering the present may be and how tempting it may be to press blindly onward into the future, the past—our past—matters. Reframing climate conversations to emphasize our shared history may help close this generational divide.

I've grown up an environmental activist. As a kid, my dad used to read me story books every night before bed, except they were not typical children's books; they were always cautionary tales about global warming usually ending with images of chopped tree stumps or little caricatures of the world burning. (And no, it was not brainwashing—looking around and seeing this imagery *actually happening* in the Amazon and Australia is even more terrifying!) After middle school, I realized I wanted to study natural sciences, ecology, and environmental studies, and no one has been able to talk me out of it since then. Throughout high school, I tried to follow that passion—spending weekdays studying innovative climate policies, and weekends in the streets of Washington, D.C., protesting the government's apathy toward implementing them.

I entered Duke University in a science and society focus group called "Science and the Public," which opened my eyes to the power and potential of science communication. In summer 2019, I completed a Huang Fellowship, training in science communication while researching saltwater intrusion and sea level rise. Through my research, I've heard from some of the brightest experts in the field, many of whom share their insights in this book. I want to focus on *their* stories—this book is an interview-driven journey.

I'm sure critics of this book would be eager to point out my age (nineteen) itself as something that disqualifies me as an author. Maybe I'm just another snowflake shouting into the void. But like many other Gen Zers, I am *ready* to be criticized for my lack of "institutional" experience.

I don't have the status of a CEO or a professor.

I don't have any climate publications in my name...yet.

I don't even have a crystal-clear picture of where the next twenty years will take me.

But I do have an idea worth sharing.

What if my generation were able to talk about the climate in a way that simultaneously respected and acknowledged the historical achievements, hard work, and successes of prior generations while maintaining a sense of urgency to collaboratively correct flaws in today's climate policy?

It is especially fitting to take time in 2020, the true fifty-year anniversary of environmental law, to look back at the 1970s and extrapolate strategies to mirror that same level of bipartisan, unprecedented environmental progress today.

Part One of this book covers the historical awakening of grassroots environmentalism, *Part Two* covers the commonalities shared between Americans through present day, and *Part Three* offers strategies to tap into those values, teaching you how to be an environmental communicator. I've spoken to local politicians, professors, CEOs, educators, marketing directors, and historians to gather expertise on this very subject. I feel compelled to write because I realized that when I spoke to people of older generations, we had much more in common than in contention—I realized that perhaps there was a way to make this all work for all of us.

My hope is that this book could appeal to anyone: teens and young adults around my age who are at least a little bit "woke" to environmental activism (folks who are more reluctant are also welcome), environmentalists or scientists of any age, and even the "Worried Middle"—concerned Americans who are aware of the problem but unsure how to act.

You may be wondering,

How do I really have an influence in an era when anyone can pass for an influencer?

How do I reconcile wanting to be involved in environmental activism and feeling inadequate just holding up a sign?

How do I best facilitate conversations with people who are older—or more conservative than I am—on climate change?

It comes down to a simple conviction:

A conviction to understand people.

A conviction to have the conversation that the dismissive phrase "okay, boomer" shuts down.

That conversation begins now.

Are you ready?

PART ONE

PLANTING THE GRASSROOTS

CHAPTER 1

THE "LITANY OF DESPAIR"

―――

A people without the knowledge of their past history, origin, and culture is like a tree without roots.

— MARCUS GARVEY

In the scholarly realm of today's grassroots Environmental Movement, we have a name for the long list of negative biological, chemical, and ecological effects humans have had on our environment: the "Litany of Despair."

Pollution. Spread of hazardous waste. Ocean acidification. Arctic ice loss. Species extinction. The Litany is *universal*— all generations have had to come to terms with it—and it is evolving; every decade has been characterized by new scientific data that informed a new addition to the list. It involves history—the "how we got here"—as much as it involves science. The Litany brings a sense of anxiety and of opportunity. The Litany is why we march.

I recently stumbled across a podcast episode titled something along the lines of "Millions of Children Coerced into Climate Strike Protest by Bad Parents."[18]

I had to listen to it, of course.

The two podcasters were not joking at all. They scoffed and scorned the popularity of #FridaysForFuture movement (the weekly school walkouts spearheaded by fifteen-year-old Swedish activist Greta Thunberg). They called the movement "foreign interference" on the youth of the United States from the UN and even questioned the validity of Greta's mental disability, calling her autism a "tactic" as well as an "amazingly convenient problem to have" to advance her environmental worldview.

Unfortunately, this 2019 podcast captures a lot of the unseen and indiscriminate backlash against the New Environmental Movement and the bold individuals like Greta who dare to become the face of it.

According to the podcasters, Friday climate strikes are a form of terrorism on children, targeting the fragile, malleable minds of our nation's youth. The podcast argues that young people, who are already prone to anxiety and insecurity "by virtue of their life stage," are being trained to consider themselves victims. "They get 'em while their brain is forming," comments one of the hosts. He repeatedly

---

18   Monica Perez and Brad Binkley, "DNB: Millions of Children Coerced into Climate Strike Protest by Bad Parents," September 9, 2019, *The Propaganda Report*, podcast, 24:44.

attributes 2019's youth climate panic to this parental "they," diminishing millions of young protesters to apparent servants, utterly brainwashed into panic, enacting their parents' socialist agenda.

The message of this podcast is beyond ironic.

We aren't being *told* to protest by our parents—we are protesting in spite of them. (In fact, a lot of our parents probably wish we'd spend a little more time in the classroom rather than playing hooky on Fridays.) A recent study from the Yale Program on Climate Change Communication actually found that among millennials, the "youngsters" of their survey, there is *less political polarization* over the issue of climate change.[19] In other words, the Republican-Democrat gap is smaller for young Americans than it is for older generations. Still, we have a long way to go before we can declare the environment a nonpartisan and age-independent issue. If there's anything I've learned from talking to my parents' generation, it's that political gridlock and protest go hand in hand. And they're no rookies when it comes to advocacy and protest.

Certainly, "okay, boomer" may be an overly dismissive or generalizing last resort against older generations, but the frustration behind the phrase is justified. We wish to respond to our own Litany of Despair in the same way Vietnam War protesters, for instance, responded to theirs. In the 1960s,

---

19 Matthew Ballew et al., "Do Younger Generations Care More about Global Warming?" *Yale Program on Climate Change Communication*, June 11, 2019.

adolescent protesters hit the streets not because their parents told them to, but because *they* witnessed the media coverage of war atrocities against civilians, grieved the deaths of their teenage brothers, and suffered firsthand the disappearance of childhood friends.

Nor are the climate strikes any product of my generation's "oversensitive" developing brains. Every scroll through our smartphones brings to our fingertips horrifying new data from IPCC reports, gruesome videos of indigenous land burning in the Amazon, and viral footage of the latest hundred-year storm (now annual) overturning cars and houses in coastal communities. Truly, part of the reason why we are "always on our phones" is because it is impossible to look away from the global environmental destruction the Age of Information has enabled us to witness. (And is my brain still developing? At two decades old, anatomically, the answer is yes. Still, I'd rather consider my mind to be "developing"—constantly processing new ideas and information—than solidifying into the dogmatic state of our dear podcasters.)

I chose to open with this rather alarming podcast episode because it starkly contrasts the real reason why adolescents march: a personal desire to bring awareness to the Litany of Despair, manifested in a group demonstration of solidarity.

A lot of it simply comes down to the worrying history lessons we've learned in school. The latter half of the twentieth century was marked by an alarming awareness of the Litany of Despair and of the Anthropocene as a whole. The history of the environmental movement can be separated into four general, overlapping stages[20] :

1. **Preservation vs. Conservation (early 1900s–1930s):** John Muir and Gifford Pinchot debated whether we should *preserve* nature for the sake of itself (keeping forests untouched) or *manage* nature responsibly to also yield products for human benefit (multiple use).
2. **Pollution (1950s–1970s):** Communities like Love Canal face serious health effects from dumping and overload of toxic chemicals released into the environment.
3. **Global Ecology and Biodiversity (1980s–1990s):** Ideological push to think of ourselves as "global citizens;" focus on tropical ecology and international agreements on saving a wide range of species.
4. **Climate Change (1990s–present):** Countries must come to terms with planet-wide change arising from the greenhouse effect and reverberating on both a local and global scale. Most of the issues in previous stages, such as pollution and biodiversity loss, are cumulative and persist alongside climate change—there has really been no "endpoint."

Likewise, the Litany of Despair can be loosely sorted by generation:

- **The Silent Generation** (born before 1945): Also called "builders." People of this generation faced questions of man's true role in nature, influenced by early writers and

---

20 Mark Kitchell, *A Fierce Green Fire: The Battle for a Living Planet* (First Run Features and Bullfrog Films, 2012), from Sundance Film Festival 2012.

philosophers such as Thoreau and Muir. Early national parks were established to preserve land, and they faced early issues of conservation versus preservation, wilderness protection, deforestation, and overhunting.

- **Baby Boomers** (born 1946-1964): Faced issues of air pollution, water pollution, unregulated chemicals and pesticides, species extinctions, fear of nuclear war, and lack of environmental law and policy framework.
- **Gen X** (born 1965-1979): Also called "baby bust." This generation faced issues of hazardous waste, concerns over energy independence, the Global Energy Crisis, and conservative backlash to environmentalism.
- **X-ennials** (born 1975-1985): This generation faced increasing concerns over ocean health, and climate change enters the conversation.
- **Gen Y** (born 1980-1994): Also called "millennials." This generation faces increased urgency of climate change, ocean acidification, and deforestation.
- **Gen Z** (born 1995-2012): Also called "iGen." This generation—my generation—is facing the network of unaddressed, irreversible tipping points caused by global climate change (see Introduction), and the possibility of global ecosystemic collapse.
- **Gen Alpha** (born 2013-2025): What this generation will face depends on our level of mobilization over the next decade. Gen Alpha will likely face the need to live in and adapt to a world defined by climate change.

What is most important is that we all, today, have at least a basic grasp of the United States' environmental track record. Regardless of whether you're a fourteen-year-old activist heading downtown to protest, a secret history buff, a business

CEO with little time to study eco-history, a nature lover, or a climate skeptic, it is impossible to fully understand the United States (or our global community) and our climate crisis today without first understanding its environmental history. Dr. Benjamin Kline, an author and environmental historian, believes environmental causes are *rooted in history*, and Americans are a product of the conquered wilderness, the Age of Exploration, colonialism, the Progressive Era, and the rise of the United States as a global power, which have all become part of our nation's environmental lore.[21]

A lot of "okay, boomer" sentiment comes from frustration at the failure of older generations to address climate change. And it's true. They failed, but only because climate change was largely off their radar. Two factors are responsible, which we must consider before leaping to antagonize the "failure" of older generations' environmental movement. First, news was only accessible through newspapers and nightly news; broadcasts aired only a few times throughout the day, unlike the 24/7 news cycle we enjoy (or despise) in the twenty-first century. Secondly, not unlike today, omnipresent lobbyists in the oil and extractive resource industries leveraged significant funding to influence government officials, and they essentially downplayed the increasing severity of climate change.[22] Activists then were as frustrated as activists are now.

---

21 Benjamin Kline, *First Along the River: A Brief History of the U.S. Environmental Movement,* 4th ed. (Lanham: Rowman & Littlefield Publishers, 2011), 1, Google Books.

22 Nathaniel Rich, "Losing Earth: The Decade We Almost Stopped Climate Change," *The New York Times,* August 1, 2018.

Global climate change has only gained widespread public attention over the past twenty-five years or so, meaning the boomers we accuse of being so ineffective were actually quite busy developing bipartisan strategies to deal with other urgent environmental concerns of their time—air pollution, water pollution, and species extinction.

One image that comes to mind is the famous photograph of the burning Cuyahoga River in Ohio, which was so polluted with industrial debris and slicks of oil that it burst into flames in 1969 (and several times earlier). The Clean Air Act, Clean Water Act, and Endangered Species Act soon followed, with support from conservatives and liberals alike. No one wanted to add flaming waterways to the Litany of Despair. In fact, it was Nixon, a Republican, who formed the Environmental Protection Agency (EPA). But during Reagan's years in the White House, a large amount of environmental protection measures were reversed or discredited. By the time climate change rose to the national agenda, it had been marginalized as a leftist issue.

In looking at a historical overview of the nation's environmental lore and movement, combined with our litany of scientific evidence on human impacts, *patterns start to emerge in how successful change-making happens.* At first, environmental action probably seems to go something like this:

Problem → Initial Outcry of Awareness → Failure to Change Policy → True Grassroots Visibility (Widespread Outcry, Sudden Catastrophe, Protest) → Success in Changing Policy

But in 1972, Anthony Downs proposed a slightly pessimistic (albeit realistic) "Issue-Attention cycle"[23]:

1. **Pre-problem stage:** An unwanted environmental problem exists, but the public has not yet been notified of its existence. Experts and organizations are already discussing the problem.

2. **Alarmed-discovery ("euphoric enthusiasm") stage:** The environmental problem receives coverage in the media and is therefore noticed by the public. The public starts pressuring the government to solve the problem.

3. **People realize significant progress will cost them:** People now realize solving the problem will cost them money, and more attention is given to the problem and potential fixes. Actions may include new legislation or other partial solutions.

4. **Public interest slowly declines:** People gradually lose interest in the topic as the media redirects its attention to other topics.

5. **Post-problem phase:** Implemented solutions lead to some institutionalization (new policies, organizations, changed attitudes, etc.). The problem now sits in the "twilight realm of lesser attention."

Does this cycle hold true today?

We'll return to the cycles of environmentalism concept later on and focus on parallels between the old and new environmental movements. What went well? What went wrong?

---

23 Anthony Downs, "Up and Down with Ecology—The 'Issue-Attention Cycle,'" *National Affairs*, no. 43 (2020, original 1972): 39–50.

We'll also explore the kind of language and media archetypes we are seeing *over and over again*, determining which tools will be most effective in weaning the country off fossil fuels, achieving net-zero emissions, and pursuing a sustainable circular economy.

The ultimate question remains in the minds of children and adults alike: *Which world leader(s), presidents, and politicians in power will be daring enough to declare the Climate Revolution that will define a new era in history textbooks?*

For my generation, we are so often told we lack the experience and political power held by older generations. That may be true for most of us, but it's rapidly changing.

And so, we march on, suspended in a hybrid sentiment of hope and grief.

CHAPTER 2

THE REVOLUTION

———

When the forest is destroyed, when the river is dammed, when the biodiversity is stolen, when fields are waterlogged or turned saline because of economic activities, it is a question of survival for these people. So our environmental movements have been justice movements.

—VANDANA SHIVA

For a moment, Wall Street was still.

Only moments earlier, young environmental activists had gathered at the Charging Bull statue at the foot of Broadway and doused its flanks in fake blood. The activists themselves, splattered in gory costume, lay motionless at the foot of the bull, the endpoint of their elaborate "funeral march." They hold homemade tombstones drawn with epitaphs like "Couldn't Outrun Wildfire" and "Drowned in Attic," warning of the gruesome deaths they predict in the wake of climate change.

It is October 7, 2019.

If the bull were not paralyzed in bronze, it would have been writhing. Dripping in red, the creature's posture transforms; its look of rugged determination and economic invincibility shifts into one of agony. Though the activists are rapidly surrounded by a sea of police officers and iPhone-toting tourists, everyone stands their ground. The chants of protesters blur into solidary silence as a single rebel begins to climb the statue. She reaches the peak of the bull's arched back and stands motionless, as frozen in time as the bronze animal below her, and raises a green flag bearing an hourglass. All that was audible in every smartphone video is the furious rippling of that flag. The spectators are hypnotized.

The chant begins cautiously: "No more bullshit. Tell the truth."

Before long, the activists' chanting swells and echoes across the New York square, completing the iconic visibility of the morning's climate change demonstration.

Then, nearly one hundred people are arrested.

It was an abrupt end to the latest "die-in" coordinated by none other than Extinction Rebellion, a youth-led climate action group born on the Parliament steps in Europe. This type of action falls well within the characteristic message of Extinction Rebellion, summarized very simply: "Together, we will peacefully occupy the centers of power and shut them down until governments act on the Climate and Ecological Emergency."[24]

---

24   "Extinction Rebellion," Extinction Rebellion website homepage, accessed Dec 17, 2019.

Does the term "die-in" sound familiar? It originated during the AIDS crisis in the 1980s, when victims of AIDS ignored by their own government traveled to the Capitol Building to take their last breaths, literally dying on the steps. Die-ins were some of the most poignant and powerful actions organized by the group ACTUP, the AIDS Coalition to Unleash Power. Even the most ignorant government can't ignore bodies. Thus, Extinction Rebellion borrowed the term "die-in" in tribute to precedent social protests like ACTUP's. The fact that they chose the Wall Street bull statue is also reminiscent of Occupy Wall Street, a transient earlier movement focused on raising awareness of extreme income inequality in the United States. What looks like a simple act of crude, gory vandalism at first glance is actually a symbolic pastiche of twentieth-century social movements.

Extinction Rebellion is already a household name in many parts of the world. The movement first took off in Europe and is now gaining traction in the United States, aiming to radically influence public perception of the climate crisis through civil disobedience. It is true that this traction has simultaneously gained them a bit of reputation.

Young people are generally on board—in a BBC survey of 3,000 people, 47 percent of eighteen to twenty-four-year-olds either "strongly supported" or "somewhat supported" disrupting traffic and public transport in the name of Extinction Rebellion's goals, referring to them as "activists" in the public eye.[25]

---

25   "What is Extinction Rebellion and What Does it Want?" *BBC News*, October 7, 2019.

Flustered adults, on the other hand, tend to favor the reference "those crazy kids," "those radicals," or some form of "those insane protestors." (Even I was guilty of this before meeting some of them.) Almost 65 percent of adults age sixty-five and older in the BBC survey opposed disruptive climate protests outright.[26] It stems from the fact that people are very protective of "business as usual." And "business as usual" shatters so profoundly during each Extinction Rebellion action that, often, bystanders late to their jobs or meetings simply seethe with frustration and mentally marginalize the protesters as "those crazy kids."

Perhaps those flustered adults are simply afraid of them.

"I'm just trying to get to the Statue of Liberty!" said one tourist.

"Get a job!" screamed another.

Looking past the dripping blood, the glued hands, and the arrests, do we actually know their story?

I, myself, have been skeptical of demonstration-centered groups in the past; as a practical thinker, I failed to realize the subtle ways in which radical protest *translates into direct action.* So, in order to make sense of "radical" perspectives, historically and now, I sat down for an interview with Sara B.*[27], a rebel I met at a Climate Strike from my university. Sara is a visiting international student from France. She only joined Extinction Rebellion recently, given that the

---

26 Ibid.

27 *Name has been changed for privacy.

international movement itself was only born in 2018. On campus, she is known as "The Activist," the girl who does it all. She took a gap semester to devote to full-time activism, spoke on climate at the National Assembly alongside Greta Thunberg, and has not quit since then. Sara is the type who tends to mysteriously disappear for time spans of a few days before suddenly returning to campus with her secretive, clever smile widened ever so slightly.

I met up with her on a breezy autumn afternoon to talk about her activism.

We sat out on the campus plaza as students bustled about all around us. She began to speak to me in her thick French accent with an apologetic disclaimer that her "English is not good." I never would have guessed that she would become one of the most eloquent speakers I've ever interviewed or that she had been arrested for the second time only days before our conversation.

I first asked her how she found the movement. She told me she started showing up to low-risk forms of civil disobedience, like marches and casual die-ins (nothing like Wall Street's), and then worked her way up to higher-risk sit-ins, blockades, and occupations ("risk" correlating to likelihood of arrest). Her passion for creating visibility around climate change seems to drown out the ever-increasing risks of public disruptions. "We have to create such a situation of crisis where they have no choice but to react on a very radical level to implement radical change, meaning attack the root of the problem. And that's when I decided to join Extinction Rebellion."

Strangely, an element of Extinction Rebellion's activism seems to be an apologetic awareness at their own nuisance:

"Sorry, but this is what we have to do."

"We've tried everything else."

"My heart is breaking and I've got to do something, and I'm putting my life on hold," commented forty-eight-year-old protester Bell Selkie, who lamented the impact of climate change on her harvests.[28] She had glued herself to the doors of a building in desperation.

Police tend to be less understanding of these displays of non-violent desperation. Sara explains to me that conflict is actually what she fears. As Extinction Rebellion becomes more direct or more demonstrative, she anticipates the almost-inevitable police violence they will face in the future. (At one event, the protest was deemed "violent" because a police officer fainted; the media neglected to mention that the cause of the officer's fainting was the police force's own tear gas.)

But what struck me most about Sara was her undying passion. Environmental activism is Sara's whole life. Some people probably see this as insanity, but in *all* great activists, at some points, there is an element of insanity (the good kind). The phrase "put my life on hold" came up a lot. As a radically dedicated activist, Sara experiences conflict in a literal sense as well as the internal "Young Activists' Conflict": wanting to

---

28   Olivia Rosane, "'I'm Putting My Life on Hold': 22 Climate Activists Arrested," *EcoWatch*, November 13, 2018.

stay enrolled in Duke, get a high degree, and make environmental change by submitting to the "expected" career pathway...but a wilder part of her wanting the courage to drop out completely, make change *now*, and disrupt a broken system. Her family members have demanded she stay in university and be "strategic" instead of leaving to pursue activism. "No. I'm suffocating. I want to help right now. I want to jump out... and I want to join. But I do not know sincerely what is best. Am I just trying to choose the comfortable solution—the conservative and self-protecting solution—when I'm thinking about university, or am I being 'strategic?'"

Spending the afternoon with Sara left me with two big takeaways. First, "radical" protest comes from a place of passion and desperation, not anger and nuisance. And second, youth-led protest groups like Extinction Rebellion operate on shock value because it *works*. Publicity, in any form, at least puts the word "climate change" on national headlines. The visibility of the Wall Street bull protest made international news, and when I had the privilege of marching alongside Extinction Rebellion in favor of a Green New Deal in Durham earlier this month, I knew exactly who they were and what they were fighting for. Sara told me it is also common for onlookers to witness a demonstration and start crying, moved by the depictions of Earth's destruction.

Though there's no denying the shock value of a group like Extinction Rebellion, a vast number of adults are active or passive supporters of the movement, and people of all ages are becoming more receptive. And although Extinction Rebellion is very reminiscent of 1960s–1970s activism, the classic image of a hippie chaining him or herself to a tree in front of a bulldozer falls short in capturing the intensity of what it means to be an activist in any era, especially in today's outcry against global climate change.

Overall, don't do what I did: judge a group prematurely for being "too radical" or not getting anything done. I realized that Extinction Rebellion, in mirroring the boldness and courage of ACTUP, Occupy Wall Street, and anti-war demonstrations, is exactly the kind of grassroots organization that may transform a movement into a revolution. By "revolution," I mean a movement that bursts out of the political sphere and into the social sphere, radically uprooting status-quo culture.

With ten years on the clock to upend and restructure our deficient climate policy, a peaceful grassroots revolution is sounding less and less radical.

Sara and I are actually now friends. The most gratifying outcome of our conversation was getting to know her. We also frequently bump into each other at climate marches.

I remember in the week following our conversation, she signed an email to me:

"With love for life and rage against its destruction,

Sara."

And, though I least expected it, her words alone gave me the desire to drop everything, don a mask, and hit the streets.

CHAPTER 3

OUR POLARIZED CLIMATE

———

The point in history at which we stand is full of promise and danger. The world will either move forward toward unity and widely shared prosperity – or it will move apart.

—FRANKLIN D. ROOSEVELT

HAPPY BIRTHDAY, EARTH DAY

About fifty years ago, on the very first Earth Day in 1970, Congress adjourned early.

It was nearly impossible to navigate the streets of larger cities like Washington, D.C., where, despite Earth Day's entirely grassroots organization methods, people showed up by the *millions* and made the cities' traffic jams (somehow) even worse for the day. New York's Fifth Avenue was closed off completely. People rallied in the streets, calling for the protection of clean air, the preservation of clean water, conservation of wild places, and for an overall recognition of our environmental citizenship.

Congress had let out early to give members the opportunity to speak at Earth Day events. Two-thirds of them ended up doing so.[29]

You heard me correctly—*two-thirds.*

Try to envision an environmental mobilization of this nature happening today. It's certainly possible in terms of numbers, as the People's Climate March, #FridaysForFuture strikes, and March for Science have attracted sizable crowds and satellite marches.

But *Congress?*

Today, Congress can barely scrape together a two-thirds supermajority on any issue or bill the fossil fuel industry has bought into. Bipartisan dedication to a grassroots event, coordinated without institutional or organizational oversight, seems nearly impossible. But they did it in 1970.

Those of us in Gen Y and Gen Z too young to have lived through the first Earth Day know little of the event other than the fact that it happened. The big takeaway is that it was *nothing* like the half-hearted attempts at roadside trash cleanups or our reluctant repetition of the vague mantra

---

29 Nicholas Lemann, "When the Earth Moved: What Happened to the Environmental Movement?" *The New Yorker,* April 8, 2013.

"Save the Earth" we've enjoyed once a year throughout our grade school curricula.

The first Earth Day was an accidental revolution.

It began after a huge oil spill in Santa Barbara, California, from a powerful explosion that spewed oil at a rate of 1,000 gallons every hour for a month, killed thousands of birds and marine animals, and cracked the sea floor in five places.[30] Horrified at the 1969 oil spill and other environmental transgressions against clean air and water, Americans were eager to support the first Earth Day one year later on April 22, 1970. (Many historians argue the 1969 oil spill and subsequent launch of Earth Day together marked the beginning of the environmental movement.) The idea of Earth Day was founded by Senator Gaylord Nelson of Wisconsin, who anticipated it would be a sort of "nationwide teach-in."[31] The congressman who served as co-chair alongside him was a pro-conservation Republican.

The sheer magnitude of the 1970 event was most alarming, both in its numerical turnout and in the scale of its bipartisanship. The estimated total number of participants was twenty million, or one in ten Americans.[32] According to a 1970 front-page article in *The New York Times*, "If the

---

30 Christine Mai-Duc, "The 1969 Santa Barbara Oil Spill that Changed Oil and Gas Exploration Forever," *Los Angeles Times*, May 20, 2015.

31 "Introduction: The Earth Day Story and Gaylord Nelson," Nelson Institute for Environmental Studies

32 Ibid.

environment had any enemies they did not make themselves known."[33]

What made Earth Day "work" so well? According to a more recent *New Yorker* article,[34]

Earth Day's success was partly a matter of timing: It took place at the moment when years of slowly building environmental awareness were coming to a head, and when the energy of the sixties was ready to be directed somewhere besides the Vietnam War and the Civil Rights Movement. A coterie of celebrated environmental prophets— Rachel Carson, David Brower, Barry Commoner, Paul Ehrlich—had already established themselves, and [recalling] the larger context: a suburbanizing, middle-class nation was increasingly aware of the outdoors and prepared to define liberalism in more than purely economic terms.

Additionally, Senator Nelson and his team were especially careful to keep Earth Day intergenerational; they structured the entire holiday around students. (Not only did they recruit a twenty-five-year-old activist Denis Hayes to lead the way in

---

33 Joseph Lelyveld, "Mood is Joyful as City Gives Its Support," *New York Times* Digital Archives, April 23, 1970.

34 Lemann, "When the Earth Moved," 2013.

organizing teach-ins, but they also deliberately picked April 22 because it was a weekday that fell between spring break and final exams!) Their goal was to maximize student participation, and it worked.

So, what would it take to repeat something like that today?

The process would certainly be much easier. Equipped with social media, high-speed data, and ample online political platforms, grassroots organizing is easier now than ever. But today's world comes with its own obstacles.

The coronavirus pandemic put us all to the test, at the exact fifty-year anniversary of the original Earth Day, as the participation of young and old activists alike depended entirely on their level of comfort using technological platforms to organize. The first ever completely online Earth Day may offer a glimpse into the future of digital activism: circulating online petitions, writing letters to Congress, signing individual carbon pledges, devoting free hours to contacting representatives...it all adds up to something more worthwhile than recycling cans.

Yet, 100 percent digital activism also raises questions about the difficulty of finding solidarity from behind a screen. As glorious and infinite as the internet may be, the tradeoff for its convenience is its absence of face-to-face human connection. There are fewer opportunities to build real intergenerational connections through Couch Activism, as activists struggle with the changing definition of what it means to "show up" online. But it's not impossible.

Luckily, I was able to "show up" to several online conversations with Frederick County Councilmember Kai Hagen, a long-time mentor and friend of mine, to get his two cents on local climate action. Kai has also served as a Frederick County Commissioner and is the founding director of Envision Frederick County, a nonprofit, nonpartisan organization dedicated to advancing a sustainable, resilient community through civic engagement.

In Kai's words, there has been "gradual but substantive growth in the public discussion on climate change." He has witnessed and facilitated that growth for decades, between "knocking on doors for the environment" in his youth, running for office later in life, and being elected. Kai explained that climate activism can be a dynamic learning experience for each one of us.

"It's about making climate change part of your personal and political lexicon."

One of the things I respect most about Kai is his emphasis on engaging youth and students in his climate work. Even during the coronavirus pandemic, he organized an online Youth Activist Panel to uplift teenage activists' stories and provide outlets for everyone to connect virtually. He also included me in a Zoom call with senior experts in the Climate Change Working Group of Frederick County. I was humbled by how much they have done for the planet. Kai skillfully uses social media and digital outreach to align the efforts of both groups. His focus on cross-generational inclusivity reminds me of the unified energy of the first Earth Day.

* * *

That's why activism and protest add up to so much more than sheer anger. Activism is about awareness, visibility, learning, and solidarity—which is why Senator Nelson chose to center Earth Day around students. And togetherness.

College campuses across the United States are well equipped to serve a second time as hotspots for Earth Day demonstrations; as professors (and local leaders) offer decades of academic expertise and credibility, and students plant seeds of excitement through digital organizing, the environment would easily become a viral and "trending" issue for the day.

What's gotten harder is actually keeping the environment a bipartisan issue—especially climate change.

UNIVERSAL VALUES

One of the most prominent historical observations of the environmental movement is that it used to be completely bipartisan.

Many of us have forgotten this.

As far back as the early 1900s, it was conservative President Teddy Roosevelt, an outspoken naturalist, who pledged to cherish the natural world and the pristine beauty of North America. It was the Rockefellers, oil billionaires, who were donors to the preservation of the U.S. Virgin Islands. The Left and the Right championed Franklin Delano Roosevelt's New Deal, including its environmental programs like the Civilian Conservation Corps, which created jobs and a sentiment of national duty and pride in restoring green spaces. And in 1970 it was Nixon, a Republican president, who created the EPA. Through its work and the work of other agencies, he passed the Clean Air Act, Clean Water Act, National Environmental Policy Act, and other laws still regarded as "bedrock" legislation that arose out of a certain desperation to protect human health. The physical conditions of metropolitan areas through the 1970s and 1980s were far more conducive to visible impacts, as the primary issues were smog, poisoned water, deafening noise and traffic, and surges in urban population numbers.

Many of these advances were dually inspired by a patriotism toward preserving the beauty of the United States' land alongside a sense of fear and urgency toward the very visible consequences of pollution, such as the burning Cuyahoga River or birds cowering in the aftermath of the 1969 oil spill. Though climate change was not yet on the national radar, protecting the environment was as universal a value as taking care of veterans or creating jobs.

Another example of visible bipartisanship was the wide circulation of famous environmental advertisements in the 70s through 80s. When I ask members of my parents' generation about their media influences growing up, I'm sure to hear about the cartoonish owl-endorsed slogan, "Give a Hoot, Don't Pollute!" or the famous "Crying Indian" ad. Certainly, looking at these well-intentioned ads from a modern critical perspective raises some questions about their long-term effects. (How much did they subtly benefit plastic companies by displacing the eco-responsibility away from mass-producing companies and onto aspiring recyclers? Why was the Native American in the "Crying Indian" ad given no speaking parts...and, embarrassingly, played by an Italian actor?)

However, the overall effect of these ads within their decade was positive. They created a certain universality in wanting to "go green," devoid of today's pessimistic attitudes about how much change an individual can actually make in his or her society. In other words, recycling was hip. The environment was not to be dominated; the air and water were inexorable parts of humanity itself that were not to be contaminated. Corruption and pollution were to be rooted out simultaneously. Politicians detected these values in their constituents and shifted their priorities accordingly, many genuinely going green themselves. In fact, there was almost no difference between Democrats' and Republicans' spending on the environment, as it became one of the least contentious issues between the two parties.

Because of these aligning values, it is entirely possible for the environment to be a bipartisan issue.

What happened?

THE GREAT "PARTISANIZATION"

It is equally inspiring and depressing to think bipartisan climate action was once at our fingertips.

The New York Times published a famous article entitled "Losing Earth: The Decade We Almost Stopped Climate Change,"[35] which captures the near-miss in policy efforts to come up with a bipartisan—and unbelievably simple—solution to climate change.

It tells the story of Rafe Pomerance, a passionate thirty-two-year-old lobbyist whose lack of scientific training made him an unlikely protagonist in almost singlehandedly bringing national attention to the climate crisis. "Losing Earth" reads like an immersive and dramatic film, very much worth settling into the couch for a one-hour rollercoaster of a read.

From 1979 to1989, we almost had it.

Pomerance had found a single alarming line in a scientific report on coal and carbon emissions and successfully carried it through the ranks to national leaders, launching an era of vigorous climate research and at last transforming the scientific story of carbon into a political story. Scientists had used computer models called "Mirror Worlds" to show possible outcomes of change to the land, ocean, and sky—and it was enough for even the heads of Exxon to favor a transition period to renewable energy.[36] United States policymakers had agreed cutting back on fossil fuels would be necessary with the simple truth: More carbon dioxide equals more warming. More warming edges us toward the tipping points.

---

35   Nathaniel Rich, "Losing Earth: The Decade We Almost Stopped Climate Change," *The New York Times*, August 1, 2018.

36   Rich, "Losing Earth," 2018, Part 1.

If there were any "partisan divide" on climate change in the 1970s, it looked nothing like the divide we're seeing today. For every anti-environment initiative President Reagan undertook in his administration—including shrinking the EPA, expanding offshore and public land drilling, and eliminating the position of science advisor—he would be challenged by members of his own party.

Robert Walker, a Republican from Pennsylvania, repeatedly criticized the U.S. government for failing to produce a single law on climate change despite the abundance of research illustrating its potentially devastating impact. "Unlike the Democrats, the Republicans demanded action," journalist Nathaniel Rich explains.[37] Al Gore, a Democrat, actually argued that persuading Congress to regulate fossil fuels would require a higher degree of certainty before such large reformations would be possible. Many scientists sided with Walker. In a way, the reverse partisan divide revealed in "Losing Earth" is not quite the foil of today's polarized climate; the debate was rooted not in *whether* to regulate fossil fuels, but how and when.

Climate advocates like Pomerance tried ardently to talk numbers, policy deliverables, and actionable goals. A carbon tax. A numerical emissions reduction goal. Listing carbon dioxide as a pollutant. Investing in clean energy. For a while, it seemed like one of these solutions would work. After the monumental international success of "closing" the ozone hole, there was a brief period of remarkable optimism from scientists, Democrats, Republicans, oil and gas executives,

---

37   Ibid.

and activists alike. One dinner party in the aftermath of the ozone success conjures a scene that is almost surreal:

... The oil-and-gas men joked with the environmentalists, the trade-group representatives chatted up the regulators, and the academics got merrily drunk. Mikhail Budyko, the don of the Soviet climatologists, settled into an extended conversation about global warming with Topping's ten-year-old son. It all seemed like the start of a grand bargain, a uniting of factions—a solution.[38]

Rafe Pomerance, James Hansen, Al Gore, and all the big-name climate advocates of the decade came so close to succeeding in that solution.

Until, as suddenly as it had taken off, the climate movement began its slow descent into muddled facts and partisanization.

This partisanization seemed to develop whenever small, unexplained inconsistencies in the climate movement received huge press attention. For example, William Nieren-berg, one of the authors of the legendary "Changing Climate" assessment who had served on Reagan's transition team, remarked out of nowhere that there was no need for urgent action on the climate.[39] The assessment called for rapid cli-

---

38   Rich, "Losing Earth," 2018, Part 2.

39   Ibid.

mate action before it's too late; Nierenberg found time during press interviews to argue the opposite. It would be better for us to proceed with caution and rely on American ingenuity. Future generations would have no problem figuring it out. The assessment itself received some press attention, but Nierenberg's contradictory speech afterward received 500 times more.[40] His words were nationally headlined and regarded as a truthfully optimistic declaration, from scientists, that we *actually had nothing to worry about.*

And so, a domino cascade of dismissiveness began.

Politicians, trained to preserve their public image and not the integrity of research, decided to procrastinate climate action, nitpicking methodologies and chasing certainty that didn't simply exist in science.

Oil and gas executives, realizing they could take advantage of the word "uncertainty" to maximize profits, started to reverse their positions on transitioning to renewable energy.

The "how and when" of climate change settled into inaction and political stagnancy.

After a series of frustrated meetings failing to produce deliverables, censorship attempts from the White House, exclusion of activists from the climate negotiations they had fought so hard to put on the calendar, and "inexplicably strident opposition" from Republican senators thought to be allies,

_____

40 Ibid.

the bipartisanship of the movement wavered.[41] Policymakers remained paralyzed by uncertainty and unwillingness to act in the face of the "lagging" consequences of climate change their generation would only have to face after comfortably retiring. Conference negotiations took place behind closed doors, shutting out activists and organizers who had discovered the issue, and the United States, under the Reagan administration, happily shirked its global responsibility to internally regulate fossil fuels in spite of the country's bipartisan political will to somehow do so.

* * *

During that fateful decade and for a while afterward, there was a downward spiral in behind-the-scenes climate policy, particularly from the oil lobby and from policymakers who personally misinterpreted the meaning of the word "uncertainty" in climate science, preventing any real or radical sweeping change on the front of global warming. It stemmed from factors as prominent as multi-billion-dollar advertising and lobbying campaigns from the fossil fuel industry to factors as subtle as President Ronald Reagan removing the solar panels that President Carter had installed on the White House roof only a few years before while in office.

The eventual goal of the oil lobby was to create dissonance around the facts of climate change, which the lobby undertook by spurring distrust in scientists and attempting to grant the false appearance of consensus (or numbers) to anti-climate scientists.

---

41   Ibid.

And there were even more technicalities at play. In the 2000 election, Al Gore lost to George W. Bush after legal turmoil and a vote recount due to "hanging chad" ballots, perhaps a climax to two decades of distrust and fraudulent operations that shielded the nation from climate realities...or maybe the United States just wasn't ready for a truly pro-environment candidate, someone who served the world and not just the nation. Still, even President Bush declared himself to be pro-environment before the issue was compromised by industry dissonance. At one point, he stood on the shores of Lake Erie and announced, "I am an environmentalist," kicking off his multi-state environmental tour. "Those who think we are powerless to do anything about the greenhouse effect are forgetting about the White House effect."[42]

But Bush himself seemed to forget about the White House effect not long afterward, as he, too, began leaning toward indecision. He was briefed by non-scientists and usually deferred negotiations to them. His chief of staff convinced him to dismiss the idea of freezing emissions in a treaty.

As soon as the "uncertainty" of climate change and the "costs" of regulating it could be construed as "anti-growth" and even "anti-capitalist," the fossil fuel industry could safely transform the issue from a non-negotiable health hazard to a conspiracy designed to infringe upon the free market. Republican beneficiaries of the fossil fuel industry ensnared monetarily as well as ideologically, quickly followed suit. After all, weren't small government and free-market economics tenets of the

---

42 Ibid.

party itself? There would be no more room for environmentalism amid dissonance.

A LEGACY OF DECEIT

It all links back to generational parallelism if we think about it this way: Fossil fuel industry dissonance is the tobacco industry dissonance of this generation. Generation X, baby boomers, and the silent generation alike have suffered from decades of misinformation surrounding the health effects of smoking. Older generations were exceptionally willing to rally around exposing the destructive health effects of Juuling and e-cigarettes for that reason. The same kind of consensus should prevail on climate change and pollution, a large portion of which could also cause detrimental respiratory damage to Americans.

Today, green initiatives are highly targeted. President Donald Trump attacks high-efficiency lightbulbs and toilets solely because of their green label. Like Reagan's solar panel removal, the act is purely demonstrative. As party loyalties prevail, it becomes an expectation to accept or reject climate change—a complex and multidisciplinary issue—along party lines, as you would an income tax or a welfare proposal. A mobilization as holistic as the climate movement is first marginalized (look at those tree-huggers), then partisanized (we can't let those tree-huggers expand our government), then forgotten (we do not have to talk about climate as it is for tree-huggers). The fossil fuel lobby strategically created enough doubt on whether climate change is caused by humans in the first place that the easiest partisan defense was to deny that statement altogether and move on.

As a result, a lot of us have also forgotten that environmental protection used to be completely bipartisan, garnering nearly unanimous agreement. Three points help console those of us who didn't get to live through that time:

1. Countless adult activists have been in the fight since they were teenagers and are willing to help.
2. Young Republicans and Democrats seem to be closing the partisan gap on climate change.[43]
3. The youth-led New Environmental Movement leaves room for bipartisanship, aligning ourselves by age and not by party.

For all young people, this decade could be our second—and final—chance.

WHEN AGE POLARIZES
"Okay, boomer."

We hear the phrase again, this time in Parliament.

Chlöe Swarbrick, the youngest member of New Zealand's parliament at twenty-five years old, was in the middle of her speech supporting a decarbonization bill when she fired the retort back at a boomer-aged Parliamentarian who interrupted her.

---

43 Kate Yoder, "On Climate Change, Younger Republicans Now Sound Like Democrats," *Grist*, September 9, 2019.

"In the year 2050, I will be fifty-six years old," Swarbrick began. "Yet, right now, the average age of this fifty-second Parliament is forty-nine years old."[44] In that moment, someone was heard heckling her in the background, scarcely perceptible. Even less perceptible was Swarbrick's unfazed response: "Okay, boomer." She reacted in a single breath and immediately continued her speech.

In the end, Swarbrick spoke eloquently and successfully defended the Zero Carbon Bill. Nonetheless, in the face of viral press attention and interviews, she worries her side comment garnered more attention than the merits of the bill itself. Swarbrick was asked where she learned the phrase. She admits it was her thirteen-year-old brother who first introduced her to it days earlier and she found herself using it unintentionally.

Her testimony aired in November 2019. #OkBoomer has since been hashtagged over 700 million times. Some say it's dead now. Others realize this is just the beginning of neo-polarization on climate change.

I have no qualms about sharing my thoughts on what Chlöe Swarbrick did. What she did was badass, especially under the time crunch of a congressional testimony. But now, amid our ten-year ultimatum to curb greenhouse gas emissions before it's too late—as well as the overwhelmingly connected digital epoch we call the Age of Information—is a throwaway remark the answer? What if instead of saying "okay, boomer,"

---

44 "New Zealand lawmaker shuts down heckler: 'OK, boomer,'" *CNN*, November 17, 2019, video, 0:14.

we took the time to continue or revive that bipartisan traction of the 1970s rather than stifle it? I hope to rally with all Gen Z-millennial snowflakes willing to cooperate with our critics and with one another to form an avalanche of change, living by the words that my boomer father taught me: "Argue to resolve; don't argue to win."

HOPE

I see the most tangible hope in RepublicEn, a movement of conservative Republicans of all ages who are pro-climate.[45] The founder of RepublicEn is Bob Inglis, an ex-representative from South Carolina's fourth district. Inglis travels across the United States talking to conservatives about how to prioritize the environment without compromising one's political identity, a shift Inglis decided to make for himself after his own teenage son inspired him (and challenged him) on the issue of climate change. "Dad, I'll vote for you...but you've gotta get your act together on the climate." Inglis told me that, in that moment, his identity as a father prevailed over his partisan identity. We'll touch more on this important shift in Chapter 5.

Inglis decided to research climate change himself and in doing so, dove deeper into his own biases on the issue. Before having that conversation with his son, Inglis mentioned climate denial was ingrained in his belief system. "All I knew was Al Gore was for it...so I was against it," he grinned.

---

45   RepublicEn.org, Energy and Enterprise Initiative.

However, he saw physical evidence of climate change for himself when he traveled to Antarctica. Ice cores, decades worth of data, and the fragility of climate-impacted landscapes all spoke to him. And so did his son.

After discovering that there are solutions agreed upon by both sides, Inglis's environmental views did a one-eighty, and he'd like to help other Republicans do the same. Inglis has been traveling around the United States on his EnCourage Tour, speaking to red states about climate solutions.

As one solution, he mentions carbon pricing as a way to promote free-market innovation without being excessively regulatory or expanding the size of government. In other words, it's revenue neutral. Money would go into the pockets of Americans, like a freedom dividend. This spend-as-you-wish dividend then goes to households, blue collar workers, white collar workers, farmers, students, and pretty much everyone except for at-the-source polluters, like Exxon. The ideal carbon fee would also be border-adjustable to imports from other countries so American markets are not disadvantaged.

In many ways, a carbon pricing solution like the one Inglis endorses is as people-centric as it gets.

Conservative voters often avoid the topic of climate change because it seems to entail drastic changes and bigger government, he explains. "It doesn't have to be that way," Inglis assures other Republicans, as he envisions new jobs, wealth creation, and more freedom in the pursuit of a new energy future. So long as government remains small and free market innovation remains big, there is no need to compromise party values for something like climate change; in fact, climate action strengthens them. "The conservative thing to do is to protect our family," he affirms.

His words come as an antidote to the divisive language like "hoax," "socialism," and "radical," which otherwise circulates at the mention of climate change.

"There are issues we can continue to disagree on and debate, but climate change doesn't have to be—and shouldn't be—one of them," Inglis told me.

If the world realizes he's right, and if his RepublicEn campaign continues to garner national attention, it may not be long before the next Earth Day attracts the largest crowds the United States has ever seen.

PART TWO

COMMON GROUND

CHAPTER 4

INTEGRATE AND INSPIRE

If a child is to keep alive his inborn sense of wonder, he needs the companionship of at least one adult who can share it, rediscovering with him the joy, excitement, and mystery of the world we live in.

—RACHEL CARSON

THE IMMORTAL INFLUENCERS

Everyone has in common the capacity to be inspired.

Do you remember what inspired you when you were young?

Think of that one lesson you were taught from an early age that has stuck with you for years or has become an intrinsic part of who you are. The first voice that inspires you after your parents'—a teacher, a mentor, a wise classmate, a favorite movie, a line from a book, or a quote from a famous role model.

Think of them as the "immortal influencers": the voices of thought leaders in the environment, or musicians, or ecofeminists, that resonate throughout history and are founded on philosophies that you, as an individual, can connect with on a deeper level. (These are people we "vibe with," as the kids say.) These are the Rachel Carsons, the E.O. Wilsons, the *Inconvenient Truths*, the "Give a Hoot, Don't Pollute"s, The *Loraxes*, the park rangers who let you hold a snake for the first time...the memorable experiences and voices that will never leave you.

According to a 2013 study, it is much easier for formative, pro-environmental influences to change your attitudes and behavior as a child than when you are an adult, acting more habitually.[46]

Most visionary thinkers will recall having an "inspired" childhood—full of role models—whether their influencers relate directly to the environment or not.

I choose the word "influencers" cautiously. No generation is better acquainted with the term "influencers" than Gen Z—when we hear it, we think of social media influencers, an army of young online personalities born out of viral popularity on Instagram, DIY modeling, aesthetic self-branding, and finding just the right angle. Their fame is judged by their ability to amass a colossal fanbase of followers and the aesthetic quality of their photographic feed.

---

46   Karen Buttigieg and Paul Pace, "Positive Youth Action Towards Climate Change," *Journal of Teacher Education for Sustainability* 15, no. 1 (June 1, 2013): 15–47.

The problem with today's influencer culture is that the buzz and popularity around social media personalities come from their ability to influence, rather than a core message or set of values. "I want to look like them" is replacing "I want to be like them." And it's easy to imitate the look of a social media influencer just by strategically posting photographs that mirror his or hers, tacking on the same labels of "eco-friendly" clothing or plastic phone cases adorned with pleas to "Save the Earth." My biggest worry is that these influencers, by nature of their ulterior self-promotion motives, perpetuate an influence devoid of meaning. Influence and activism are not the same thing.

This is not to say Gen Z influencers can't be—or haven't been— using their powers for good. Some of the most successful and widely circulated accounts on the internet right now include young people who have devoted their lives to climate action: @gretathunberg, @autumn.peltier, and @xiuhtezcatl, all of whom set a strong example of how to pursue a true activist lifestyle rather than just promoting the greenwashed image of one. Greta didn't just talk about carbon emissions—she opted to set sail across the North Atlantic rather than traveling by airplane. Autumn, an indigenous activist who learned about the sacred nature of water from her great-aunt, was named chief water commissioner by the Anishinabek Nation when she was only fourteen years old.[47] ("One day, I will be an ancestor," Autumn famously shared.)[48]

---

47   "Meet Autumn Peltier, Teen Water Warrior," CBC Podcasts, last modified August 6, 2019.

48   "Indigenous Teenager to Advocate for Clean Water in Canada at United Nations Forum," CFWE Radio, September 26, 2019.

These influencers encourage their followers to do more than passively consume their social media feed, instead urging them to get involved locally and politically, largely by example.

Research has a name for maintaining this type of active engagement: the "locus of control."

The "locus of control" refers to the sense that [we] have the ability to influence the outcome of a situation and can help children and young people develop a sense of empowerment and personal responsibility. Research has found that "internal locus of control" is the core variable for improving the intention to act for responsible environmental behaviour. Therefore, it is important to stimulate the internal locus of control by [...] encouraging people to make their own decisions about problems and critically evaluate the opinions of others and by providing opportunities for people to apply action skills successfully.[49]

If you remember the "Issue-Attention" cycle from Chapter 1, movements tend to die out as people simply lose interest or lose the belief that they're able to make a difference on an

---

49 Carla Wilson, "Effective Approaches to Connect Children with Nature," Department of Conservation Te Papa Atawbai, (July 2011): 7.

issue. The locus of control helps reverse this. It helps young (and old) people become autonomous activists.

One salient example that comes to mind is the ardor with which young people hit the streets in the 2020 Black Lives Matter protests. Activists also mobilized and made phone calls, signed petitions, wrote letters, and donated money to bring reformative justice to George Floyd and victims of police brutality. Older activists were also integral in providing expertise, resources, institutional reforms, and protest safety tips. Together, people were *influenced* by the flood of social media awareness, but also *engaged*. Protestors acted outside of social media, as we all were challenged to look metaphysically at its shortcomings (i.e. retweeting, then being silent).

* * *

Carla Wilson, who devised the term "locus of control," also studied the intersections between conservation and education and came up with the following list of successful tactics to engage, rather than just "influence," youth in an environmental context:

- Make it relevant to everyday life.
- Foster the role of "active stakeholder."
- Promote direct experience.
- Include families, communities, and role models.
- Provide opportunities for social connections.
- Target real local issues.
- Promote collective action.

Where some traditional education settings fall short in these strategies, young activists on social media pick up the slack. The young activists who focus on pursuing these strategies on and off of social media, and focus on leading by example, inspire more change than those who solely promote green brands and clothing businesses, or tweet emptily and then "log off" of activism for the day.

Despite—or because of—their young age, activists like Greta Thunberg and Autumn Peltier are on track to become immortal influencers, joining the ranks of John Muir, Chico Mendes, Wangari Maathai, and others whose courageous work touches the hearts of people.

INTEGRATING THE ENVIRONMENT INTO LESSONS AND CONVERSATIONS

I remember my earliest environmental influences being Jane Goodall, the Pixar film *Wall-E*, Sugarloaf Mountain, Sylvia Earle, Rachel Carson....

. . . And my fifth-grade teacher Mr. Jeff Esko.

I recently reconnected with Jeff, whom I hadn't seen for almost ten years, and we met up for lunch. Jeff has an exquisite mind and an unconventional teaching style. Several days out of every week, he would take our jittery class of thirty-six down to the Great Heron Wetlands, a beautiful pond ecosystem nestled on the perimeter of our elementary school grounds. He always worked tirelessly behind the scenes to preserve the wetlands and craft lesson plans around them.

When he first found the wetlands area, it was a ditch. Jeff realized the ditch was actually a cold-water *spring*, which happened to be right on the school's property. He turned it into a gift for all of us—he coordinated soil conservation surveys, wrote applications and grants, and had two ponds blueprinted and built using the spring source. Soon, the wetlands had a path leading down to it, a small boardwalk, a wildflower meadow, classroom benches, and a fossil wall. It was a curious fifth grader's heaven.

We would spend afternoons down in the wetlands, trying our hand at nature photography, making drawings of alien-like water microbes we viewed under microscopes, and learning the geological and cultural history of the Maryland land surrounding our school.

One day we even threw a pow-wow with local Native American tribes. Over 700 students showed up, joining alumni, teachers, and tribal leaders, to celebrate the month of the Native American and the ten-year anniversary of naming the "Great Heron Wetlands." By officially naming it and designating it as a geographic landmark, Jeff explained, it would be harder for it to be destroyed. The land all around was sacred—not just because he discovered it was the resting place for fallen soldiers in the Civil War, but because it was now a refuge for so many of us, of all ages, to come together and honor nature.

At the pow-wow, all of us celebrated by joining hands in a beautiful snake dance out in the fields. Next to us stood a tall teepee, unexpectedly adjacent to a solar-panel display that powered the waterfall and fountain in one of the ponds.

As we spiraled in our dance, I felt the sacredness of environmentalism—and the land we stood on—for the first time.

It seemed Jeff had always felt it. "The chanting and the drumming…that goes right to your soul."

Jeff is someone whose soul has been touched by music, and he has a strong background in it. He played in a band in the 1960s, Esko Affair, whose music I greatly enjoyed hearing as we talked. He's always lived kind of a double life, teaching by day and playing music (now, the lute in a Celtic band) by night.

He shared with me the songs that resonate with him—among them, Joni Mitchell's "Big Yellow Taxi" (he remarked, "… we *unpaved* paradise and put up a wetlands,") and John Prine's moving "Paradise," which is written as a conversation between a father and son in which the son learns that his favorite childhood spot has been strip-mined by Peabody Coal Company.

One of the qualities I admire most about Jeff is the diversity of the artists, thinkers, and philosophies that inspire him.

He mentioned his personal and cultural transformation stirred by Ravi Shankar's sitar music, the Monterey Pop Festival (1967), Herman Hesse's *Siddhartha*, the writings of Lao Tzu, and transcendental meditation, all of which brought Eastern thought to the West. He also noted the issues being protested *then* are the same issues being protested today, particularly civil rights, violence, and the environment.

His childhood also provided inspiration. Jeff lived two blocks away from a linear park in Philadelphia along Pennypack Creek, where he'd find salamanders, turtles, and deer, as well as the peace and solace of escaping from "the craziness of growing up." It sounded like the same sense of peace the wetlands brought me.

After spending time living on a farm with lots of kids around, Jeff eventually realized he had an affinity for teaching and inspiring young children. "I thought, what better thing to do in the world. To educate people...and help people." For a while, he assumed he'd be a music teacher, but quickly realized he wouldn't be able to (sanely) teach it 24/7. Instead, his mind kept coming back to science, history, literature, and the intersections of each. Picking a single subject seemed counterproductive—and futile. So, he started teaching elementary school.

The thing to remember about elementary school is that you're getting one teacher for four or five different subjects: math, social studies, English, and science. Prior to fifth grade, transitions between subjects typically included a two-minute stretch break (if we were lucky), followed by a phrase along the lines of, "Okay, time to switch gears now. Put away your science binders and take out your English binders." The approach was jarring; abrupt transitions between subjects allowed little time or space to take a snack break, let alone draw interdisciplinary connections between class content.

Jeff attempted to subvert this issue by threading content together across disciplines, in what he calls an "integrated curriculum," a style he learned during his Fulbright in Nottingham, England.

He would read us Native American myths about our connection to nature and science, bring out his guitar to sing environmental songs together, and have us write creative poems about the creatures we found in the wetlands. He was also the first teacher I remember who shared his genuine love and respect for Native American culture with us, rather than reciting the offensively simplified Thanksgiving Day lessons that so many early-ed classrooms resorted to. The immortal influence of Chief Seattle, Bobby Littlebear, and other indigenous environmentalists, quickly ingrained in our minds the notion that human beings are one with our environment, rather than hierarchical beings that preside over it. "This is not water, but the blood of our ancestors," he told us, poignantly referencing Chief Seattle.

An integrated curriculum like Jeff's matters because the environment is inherently interdisciplinary; it is harmful to think of the environment as a separate "other." In environmental activism, it is *valuable* to know how the climate connects to history, music, mathematics, economics, and ecology. An integrated curriculum helps you become an integrated human being, versed in diverse disciplines and inspirational sources.

FREE-CHOICE LEARNING: THE AGENCY TO BECOME ENVIRONMENTALISTS

One day, Jeff took us on a field trip to the Smithsonian Museum of Natural History and set us loose inside. It wasn't total chaos, however. He gave us each a twelve-page study guide to fill out . . .which may sound horrific but actually gave us a certain freedom to go engage with the museum and find the answers for ourselves. There was no tour guide lecturing us. This sort of "free-choice learning," meaning the individualistic learning that happens outside of lecture-and-listen settings, is a simple way to inspire anyone to (voluntarily) care about the environment, exploring and gaining interest *on their own terms.* (Other museum patrons saw the notes we were taking and compared Jeff's lessons to "college curriculum.") I kept my study guide and still have it today.

"Through these experiences," concludes one study, "'the learner exercises a large degree of choice and control over the what, when and why of learning. [...] Free-choice learning represents a bottom up, individual-driven way to think about learning rather than a top-down, institution-driven view."[50]

This distinction is important: bottom-up learning inspires grassroots thinking.

Conservation research also praises this self-guided approach, listing camping, walking in National Parks, and exploring wildlife sanctuaries and gardens as experiences proven to be most memorable and influential for the young and old. And indeed, they were. After decades of award-winning teaching, I liked to think Jeff was an educator who could make a naturalist out of anyone.

---

50   Ibid, 6.

THE TAKEAWAYS

I believe all educators, activists, and environmental communicators can learn two things from Jeff. First, have the courage to do your own thing when it comes to the environment. Certainly, his style of teaching did not adhere to the standardized public school fifth-grade curriculum (and our class took a couple of covert Saturday field trips)—but that was the greatest blessing of it. By creating outside-the-box integrated lessons, Jeff was the role model that actually turned me into an environmentalist.

And second, it is never too late to get an education or to change your perspectives on the world.

Jeff had lost most of his eyesight, tragically and ironically, due to the environmental conditions of the portable classroom he worked so hard in for seven years; high levels of volatile organic compounds and hypoxia in the HVAC system damaged his optic nerve. These chemicals were *banned* in portable classrooms in California under Proposition 65.

Still, despite my disbelief and horror, he remained as energized and optimistic as anyone remembers him. "I can still read," he informed me excitedly. He placed a stack of environmental literature—Terry Tempest Williams, E. F. Schumacher, Rachel Carson—in front of me on the table. Even a decade later, in his injury and in his retirement, he is still trying to help me learn. He will always be a teacher. And this is part of true grassroots influence: always welcoming new teaching and learning.

* * *

In closing, the message he wrote on our fifth-grade wetlands calendars reminds me of his life's mission:

Dear Friends,

As we celebrate the Circle of Life in the Great Heron Wetlands, as seen through the eyes of our 2010-2011 fifth grade student photographers and other contributors, we realize the beauty and resilience of nature. As we teach social awareness of environmental issues, we produce informed citizens. Social action and community cooperation have enabled the Great Heron Wetlands committee to create a healthier environment, protecting our Great Heron Wetlands as well as benefiting the water quality of our precious Chesapeake Bay. Let us continue to make wise choices and take positive action as we see the Circle of Life spiral into the future.

Peace,

Jeff Esko

Chair of the Great Heron Wetlands

THE FUTURE OF INSPIRATION

The unfortunate reality is that, in the United States, the majority of K-12 and college science classes still do not devote any class time to teaching (or even discussing) climate change material, even though 86 percent of teachers surveyed indicated they want to include it in their curriculum.

(Not to mention four in five parents!)[51] This may be one of the reasons why conversations between older and younger generations about climate change tend to feel rather prickly—academic discourse around it has been essentially silenced by older administrators and parents, who consider a planetary change unit too frivolous or too ideologically dangerous for their children to undertake.

Following the model of free-choice learning, it should ultimately be up to the students themselves to decide what they learn about their own planet and about the consensus of scientists within it.

I can only hope other children have space to do so, and space to prioritize the inspiring voices of environmental role models at the forefront of their hearts and minds.

"We are nothing without our elders," writes Xiuhtezcatl Martinez, an indigenous activist and hip-hop artist, in a social media post.[52] "Our storytellers, wisdom keepers, our guardians, our medicine keepers, those that paved the path and carried the culture so the younger generation could run with it." He urges us to rebel against the colonial culture of treating our elders as disposable. Instead, we must protect them. "They are our bridge to our ancestors."

Driven by the motivation of great thought leaders and by sense of deeply rooted unity with the Earth, children are

---

51 Anya Kamenetz, "Most Teachers Don't Teach Climate Change; 4 In 5 Parents Wish They Did," April 22, 2019, in *NPR Morning Edition*, radio show.

52 Xiuhtezcatl Martinez (@xiuhtezcatl), Instagram post, March 14, 2020.

already rising as grassroots leaders with their own messages to share and pass on. There is nothing more exciting than seeing this next wave of immortal influencers assembling, not just on social media, but at UN Climate Conferences and on Capitol Hill. Today, we will be influencers.

One day, we will all be ancestors.

CHAPTER 5

PARTISANSHIP AND PARENTHOOD

———

Is not the sky a father and the earth a mother, and are not all living things with feet or wings or roots their children?

—BLACK ELK

#NOFUTURENOCHILDREN

As I am writing this, I have five days left of being a teenager.

I'm sure a lot of readers have experienced this feeling—or are also counting down to it—the existential brink of two decades is somehow much heavier than a mere eighteen or nineteen years. But I'm focused on something else, a much more childish realization: Because I was born in the year 1999 specifically, I have a rare opportunity in front of me. If I can just make it through the 2000s and into year 2100, I will be able to proudly announce that I have technically lived through a span of three centuries and two millennia. If phrased correctly, my longevity will rival that of Master Yoda, the *Star Wars* character famous for aging over 800 years.

Selfish aspirations for Yoda-hood aside, the reality is I have no idea how long I'll survive, whether I'll have children, or whether 2100 is a year I'd even want to see. But all three of these uncertainties are prevailing questions in the realm of modern environmental activism. Amid climate chaos, the longevity and quality of human life are in jeopardy. We see it in the way Greta Thunberg trembles at the microphone when addressing the politicians who failed her. We see it in the very core of Extinction Rebellion's mission statement. We see it online. Believe it or not, there's an online pledge stating, "I pledge not to have children until I am sure my government will ensure a safe future for them," and already 5,337 young people have signed it.

Emma Lim, the eighteen-year-old founder from Ontario, justifies her audacious pledge:

"I want my children to see all of the beautiful things I see. I want them to go swimming in the ocean with me. I want to take them camping in the summer, and for drives to see the changing leaves in the fall. I want to go sledding with them. I want to teach them how to grow a garden. I want my children to be free to chase their dreams, but everything will be more expensive with climate change.

I am facing a future of economic instability, of food scarcity and extreme weather. What if I have to sacrifice my child's education to pay for a new house? What if my house becomes uninsurable? What if I have to pay for clean water?

What if my city becomes unsafe and I have to flee or if my baby is sick, but the hospitals are overflowing with people fleeing worse conditions? For many people these fears are already reality.

I am giving up my chance of having a family because I will only have children if I know I can keep them safe. It breaks my heart, but I created this pledge because I know I am not alone. I am not the only young person giving up lifelong dreams because they are unsure of what the future will hold. We've read the science, and now we're pleading with our government.

Please, keep us safe. Please act while there is still time."[53]

EMMA LIM

And so, the somewhat morbid hashtag #NoFutureNoChildren was born, a testament to the urgency of the Intergovernmental Panel on Climate Change's ten-year ultimatum. Waves of similar birth-strikes, as they are called, have already permeated the United States and global media outlets. It's important to understand the motives for embracing or rejecting parenthood in the face of climate change.

THREE CAMPS

Keeping Emma's reasoning in mind, attitudes toward parenthood in the face of climate change can be divided into three camps. (The implied "fourth camp" being people who

---

53   John Bacon, "No Future, No Children: Teens Refusing to Have Kids Until There's Action on Climate Change," *USA Today*, September 29, 2019.

don't factor climate change into their parenthood decisions at all.)

The first camp simply rejects the idea of having children altogether. One twenty-one-year-old student who attended the annual Uplift Climate conference (nicknamed the "climate change depression session" by one attendee), confidently stated in an NBC report that she would not be having kids.[54] "I'm definitely not having kids. I don't have hope that we will avoid climate catastrophe. The changes that need to happen aren't happening." Another attendee explains that she no longer talks about future parenthood with her own children or launches into "You'll be such a good dad" with her son because it "feels wrong."

The second camp rests on uncertainty. "If I did have kids," comments a twenty-six-year-old *Uplift* attendee, "they would have the worst life ever." However, after an environmental scientist encouraged her that raising a climate-conscious child would potentially be better than abstaining from ever having kids, her anxiety dissipated. She is now unsure of what to do.

Finally, the third camp is pure optimism toward having children during a climate crisis. It is possible to raise a generation of environment defenders, and in a sense, we're already seeing that happen. One young man, about to become a father, asserts that his baby brings him a sense of hope.

---

54   Avichai Scher, "'Climate Grief': The Growing Emotional Toll of Climate Change," *NBC News*, December 14, 2018.

"It's the most positive affirmation I can make about the future. We aren't giving up. This is a multigenerational problem."

What can we make of this? And how would you, personally, define a "safe" world? Regardless of which camp your friends and family members fall into—or you see within yourself— that soon-to-be father is absolutely correct that the problem of climate change is multigenerational. The successful fight against urban air and water pollution throughout the 1970s and 1980s stemmed from the same doctrine: We want the planet to be habitable for everyone who comes after us. It's also the classic rule of cleaning up: Leave the room better than you found it. We want the best for our children.

Parenthood is universal, and with it, care for the well-being and health of children. According to a 2018 Yale study, providing a better life for our children and grandchildren is the number one most common reason why Americans want to reduce global warming.[55] That's why some researchers have actually studied parenthood as a lens—perhaps *the* lens— that can be used to overcome political divides toward climate change. Their discoveries are remarkable.

---

55 Anthony Leiserowitz et al., "Climate Change in the American Mind: March 2018," *Yale Program on Climate Change Communication*, April 17, 2018.

PUT ON YOUR PARENTHOOD GLASSES

Dr. Emily Diamond, now an assistant professor at the University of Rhode Island, wanted to find out how to reframe the climate change debate in a way that could bridge the partisan divide.

For her study, she designed an online survey that would have two groups of participants: one group would be asked a bunch of questions about their partisan identity at the start of the survey, and the other group would receive questions about their parental identity.[56] (The "Partisan" group might be asked which political party they belong to and how much it matters to them; the "Parent" group would be asked if they were a parent, how many children they had, etc.)

These early survey questions were designed to *prime* the Partisan or Parent identity of survey participants, meaning draw that identity to the forefront of their mind.

Then, everyone received the same message about climate change and future generations, an excerpt from a UNICEF report warning that children would be most vulnerable to the devastating effects of climate change. The report specified that children will face hunger and malnutrition as food production is compromised by increased flooding and droughts.

Finally, Diamond asked participants to indicate their levels of climate change concern, their support for various climate

---

56   Emily P. Diamond, "The Influence of Identity Salience on Framing Effectiveness: An Experiment" (in press, 2020), *Political Psychology*.

policies, and their willingness to undertake political behaviors to support climate policies.

She wondered, *Would participants' level of climate change concern* change *depending on whether they'd been primed as Democrats/Republicans or as parents?*

Actually, the answer is yes. Republicans primed to think of themselves as parents were 12 percent more likely to express concern about climate change and undertake political behaviors on climate policy.[57]

One in ten may not seem like a revolutionary proportion, but this kind of a shift could be the difference in Congress. What Diamond and her team succeeded in doing in this study was to create a group of like-minded parents, not partisans.

Her study also opens up questions about which other social identities could be salient in grassroots climate advocacy. Social identities aren't just political; they might pertain to religion, race, age, or gender. I'm sure you can add several more groups to this list, as identity politics continue to define today's political climate (in fact, several studies have shown that opinions toward climate change are driven by *identities* more than facts)![58] Identity politics may prove to be the greatest tool in the future of grassroots climate advocacy.

Let's come back to the Parental identity group. In an episode of the *Ways and Means* podcast on climate change, they

---

57   Ibid, 16-20.

58   Ibid, 7.

come up with a really useful analogy on the lens of Parenthood: a pair of glasses.[59]

Picture it this way: A seventy-five-year-old woman (let's call her Mary) sits at her desk, frustrated, scrolling through her Facebook feed. She is bombarded with political advertisements and posts, many of which condemn the "liberal agenda" of climate change policy. Because they come from sources and commentators she trusts, she expresses her agreement in the comments. During that time, she is wearing her partisan "glasses."

Later that day, Mary logs off her computer. Her grandchildren come to visit, and she takes them outside to do some gardening. Complimenting her on her green thumb, Mary's grandkids enjoy the outdoors with her and express their concern for the planet. In that moment, her partisan glasses are off; instead, she's wearing her grandmother glasses, or her gardener glasses, or her caretaker glasses. Her list of possible identities goes on. She could also be wearing her rural-resident glasses, her steward glasses, or even her student glasses, listening carefully to her grandkids talk about how tangibly and immediately climate change is jeopardizing crop yields in Asia. Mary's partisan predispositions have been temporarily left behind, as she has swapped "glasses" in that outdoor setting with her grandchildren. And climate change is not theoretical to her grandchildren.

---

59   "How Parenthood Affects Climate Change Skeptics," *Ways and Means Podcast* (transcript), Sanford School of Public Policy, September 2020.

(Grand)parenthood, however, is tied so closely to unconditional love and sacrifice that it seems to overpower parti-
sanship, or at least induce a level of trust that makes anyone
slightly more receptive toward climate concern. The idea of
intergenerational justice, or making a better world for future
generations, prevails in getting policymakers to care about
this crisis; notably, Barack Obama framed part of his final
speech in office around justice for future generations.[60]

But research has also shown Obama's words probably
wouldn't make it the past partisan walls of those who disagree with him on other issues. People tend to selectively
accept or reject evidence of climate change risk depending
on how much they believe the experts share their worldviews —in other words, it all depends on who's delivering
the information.[61]

Family ties might be the strongest way to circumvent this
phenomenon. Parents listen to children; children listen to
parents. Often, parents listen to other parents. The foundations of love and respect that bring a family together are
absent in online political media driven by hatred, scandal,
and a robust "us versus them" attitude. But that's where we
find the strength of word-of-mouth climate communication;
in a civil discussion between trusted individuals, partisan
predispositions disappear. Likewise, liberal-leaning activists
would benefit from removing their partisan glasses when
contemplating intergenerational justice. There is nothing

---

60 Diamond, "The Influence of Identity Salience on Framing Effectiveness,"
    9-10.

61 Ibid, 7.

political about wanting to leave a positive legacy for one's children. That genuine desire may be what helps us transcend political roadblocks (distrust in government, hesitation toward government regulation) as market-driven solutions continue to emerge.

RepublicEn founder Bob Inglis, who told his story in Chapter 3, remembers the exact moment his eighteen-year-old son promised to vote for him but urged him to take climate change seriously. "What he was really saying...was, Dad, I love you." Inglis knew it then, and he feels it intensely to this day. "You can be better than you were before and be relevant to my future and my four sisters' futures."[62] His son's words prompted him to join the congressional delegation to Antarctica in the first place. Inglis's personal story carries a particular importance in the Eco-Right movement because it proves he can maintain his Republican, small-government identity and his climate-conscious parental identity simultaneously (which, in light of the *Ways and Means* analogy, would conjure a somewhat humorous mental image of multiple pairs of glasses worn at once).

I received more insights on family ties from an activist named Kat Horvath, who is an organizer in the youth-led Sunrise Movement. A lot of her work revolves around simply giving young people the tools to *show up*—coordinating carpools, sign-ups, and trainings for Sunrise events.

The goal of the Sunrise Movement is to create an army of climate-conscious young people and build political momentum

---

62   "How Parenthood Affects Climate Skeptics," 1.

around a Green New Deal and job creation. In many ways, Sunrise itself was born as a "child" movement to parental predecessors such as the Sierra Club and the Occupy Wall Street Movement (though the latter serves as an example of a movement that "fizzled out;" Sunrise aims to *maintain* momentum where Occupy Wall Street failed to do so after initially capturing the public's attention).[63] Activists like Kat have learned from previous movements to leverage an online social media presence (Twitter especially) and allies from older generations (Bernie Sanders especially), both of which have made the movement hugely successful in its publicity.

While Inglis gained his environmental conscience from his son, Kat gained hers from her mother. "I've been interested in environmental stuff since I was a kid," she explained. Like many of the other activists I talked to in this book, she was taught to be a steward of her home on Earth from a young age—in this case, by her mom. "I think my sister and I really learned by watching her."

I asked Kat if she thought that pattern went both ways. Can older people, too, *become* environmentalists?

"I've noticed it's a pretty natural progression," Kat said. She noted the large demographic of "grown-up hippies" (I chuckled at the term): open-minded parents who are at least familiar with the passion underlying the cause, even if they remain

---

63 Mark K. Matthews, Nick Bowlin, and Benjamin Hulac, "Inside the Sunrise Movement (It Didn't Happen by Accident)," *E&E News*, December 3, 2018.

more passive, non-action supporters of climate advocacy like her dad.

Though Kat is several decades younger than Inglis and significantly older than Emma Lim when she wrote the #NoFutureNoChildren pledge, all of their insights point to an illustrative truth in the climate movement:

The love and loyalty of parenthood is powerful.

WHAT OUR PARENTS TEACH US

It's amazing how many stories people carry quietly within themselves. Stories distilled by the sense of humility that accompanies aging, stories harbored as little else than fond memories—no matter how legendary they may come across to their captivated audience. The stories are always part of the storyteller. Only occasionally are these memories stirred or shared upon request, and they are uttered with such nonchalant nostalgia that the fortunate listener wishes only to have asked earlier.

When my twin brother and I were much younger, we undervalued the idea of listening to stories from our parents' pasts. The ordeal was always somewhat forced, as our mom would bribe us to join her on the couch and watch slides of her adventures in Japan, France, Ireland, and across the world performing music; with our ten-second attention spans, it felt like a chore to sit still on the couch and watch our parents' pasts unfold as the archaic slide projector whirred and clicked in front of us. Taking an interest in their coming of age was difficult when we had yet to experience our own.

Then, as we entered secondary school, I developed an inexplicable and sudden curiosity toward every detail of my parents' pasts. What kind of students were they? How did they navigate their twenties? Their careers? How did they meet? For the first time, my brother and I began talking with them as fellow adults, and on that equalizing platform of adulthood, it came more naturally for us to take a keen and genuine interest in the stories that had shaped their characters. My motive extended beyond the practicality of seeking life advice on traveling, careers, and making a difference. I wanted to know my parents; I wanted to understand what made them who they are.

Frantically, I vowed I would devote time to finding out.

I discovered, after hours of coffee and conversation with my mom, that her musical performances were not the frivolous spectacles I had imagined as a child. She was actually part of *Up with People,* a world-traveling musical group whose mission is to promote world peace through song and dance. From 1984–1986, my mom performed in dozens of countries, formed lifelong relationships with international host families, volunteered in each community, and even performed in the halftime show of Super Bowl XX. "It was one of the best moments of my life," she casually said to me, holding up a grainy YouTube video of *Up with People*'s performance.

In each and every performance, beneath its endearing layers of cheesy 1980s glory, my mom and her traveling cast projected a vision of harmony and peace between nations. And that formative experience, I discovered, shaped her into more than just a performer. She had become an activist in her own unique way. She had grown up in the grassroots.

* * *

My dad's story is a little different, as he jumped directly into environmental work as a young adult.

His adventure began when he worked for the Alaska Coalition at age twenty-two, fresh out of college. (And his job search turned out to be remarkably simple: "I went home to the Washington, D.C., area, went in, and asked.")

Even as a young intern, he proved himself through his think-outside-the-box approach to activism; the stories he told were surprisingly laced with ingenuity, secrecy, and strategic risk-taking.

One sweltering summer day in August 1980, my dad sat on a bus riding home from D.C. He was on his way back from a secret strategy meeting with the Alaska Coalition staff and directors of lobbying.

A Senate vote was coming up on the Alaska National Interest Lands Conservation Act (Alaska Lands Act), a piece of legislation proposing to set aside protected land in Alaska, which was currently opposed, unfortunately, by none other than the Alaskan senators themselves. Senator Mike Gravel, especially, decided he would rather keep the state open to oil, gas, mining, and timber industries, and started filibustering the conservation bill when it came up in the Senate. Senator Gravel became the worst enemy of his own state's landscapes.

However, the Coalition staff and their Senate supporters had a plan: They would cut off his filibuster with what was called a "cloture vote." With a sixty-vote majority, the Senate could override the filibuster.

To avoid leaking their strategy prematurely, the Coalition staff were explicitly told not to talk to any journalists, stakeholders, or the media.

My dad was mulling over all of this in his head on the bus ride, sweating from the heat and nervous uncertainty as to whether the filibuster could be stopped.

Out of nowhere, he saw a familiar face board the bus: an old buddy from high school who had since become a journalist for a major newspaper.

As soon as he saw my dad, he approached him and sat down. The two enjoyed catching up for a few minutes.

"What have you been up to?" he asked my dad.

"I've been working with the Alaska Coalition on the Alaska Lands Act."

The journalist's eyes widened, his interest piqued. He started peppering my dad with all kinds of questions, each one a reminder of the lobbying director's warning. It was time to start playing dumb.

"What's going to happen?"

My dad chose his next move carefully. He decided to play the *I'm just a little intern; I don't really know what's going on* card, and in his words, "totally clammed up." He mumbled polite one-word answers to the journalist until he was able to slip off the bus.

"It was kind of a funny story," my dad recalls, "and that friend still gives me a hard time about it to this day, because he found out afterwards how I clammed up and wouldn't say anything."

(His anecdote teaches us an unlikely lesson: Sometimes, activism is about knowing when not to talk.)

Not long afterward, my dad pulled more strings for the Alaska Coalition. The Coalition asked him to stay and hired him as a full-time grassroots coordinator, meaning he made phone calls every week to activists in six different states, mobilizing everyone prior to a House or Senate vote.

There was one Texas senator in particular, named Lloyd Bentsen, whose support would be very valuable to the Coalition. *How do we get this guy on our side?*

My dad discovered the senator would be boarding an Air Force One flight back to D.C. alongside President Jimmy Carter after his brief stay in Texas.

What most people saw as a routine travel arrangement, my dad saw as a creative opportunity to create political pressure. He quickly reached out to one of his most powerful, pro-conservation grassroots contacts, Texas Land Commissioner Bob

Armstrong, with a bit of a weird ask: Buy a ticket to Washington on Air Force One alongside these two men. Armstrong had always believed in the protection of public lands, and he instantly agreed to tag along. The stage was ready. As a twenty-three-year-old intern, my dad coordinated a decisive seating arrangement: On one side of Senator Bentsen, Land Commissioner Bob Armstrong; on his other side, the President of the United States, both simultaneously (and politely) lobbying him to vote in favor of the Alaska Lands Act all the way back to D.C. It worked—he later voted accordingly.

My dad paused and chuckled as he recalled that memory. He shifted his weight in the cozy armchair he reclined in for our interview. It was a true dad chair, I decided, that supported an activist now in his sixties. We spoke together in a cold hotel room. The thermostat had been meticulously adjusted to minimize energy consumption, just like every room I'd grown up in as a child.

"It was kind of a major coup for a twenty-three-year-old kid right out of college to be orchestrating that to happen," he continued, a faraway look returning to his green eyes. It was the first time I heard him take pride in the youthful ingenuity he displayed in his early career. (So did his supervisors and lobbying directors—they paid for everyone's Air Force One flights and admitted how impressed they were by the seating plan.)

* * *

On a day even closer to the final vote on the full Senate floor, the Coalition needed the support of Senator Richard

Schweiker from Pennsylvania. Senator Schweiker's son had been my dad's childhood best friend and next-door neighbor from ages four to twelve, so his father was very receptive to meeting up again for old times' sake. My dad called up the Senator and arranged to have lunch at his home on a Saturday afternoon.

They began talking about the bill over lunch, and in spite of Senator Schweiker's fairly conservative political leanings, he seemed interested and open-minded toward the topic of protecting land. It seemed his main concern stemmed from whether oil and gas reserves would still be accessible or if they would be blocked off entirely in protected National Parks. Understanding his economic hesitation, my dad brought out a physical map of the public land conservation units and showed him that many of the natural resource areas would not be blocked off. It was a reasonable compromise. Neighbor-to-neighbor, friend-to-friend, they reached this conclusion, and the Senator ended up voting pretty well in favor of the Alaska Lands Act.

It turns out compromise was the key to victory for this bill. In 1980, Reagan won the election, and the Alaska Coalition decided it would be better to support a compromise-infused version of the bill, one that would pass immediately, than to stubbornly promote a "perfect" version of the bill that would be delayed until after Reagan's inauguration alongside a new, more conservative session of Congress (and risk it getting killed completely after ten years in the making). The compromised version was still a great bill, my dad noted, and "did fabulous things for land conservation in Alaska." And it passed.

"You have to be reasonable at times," he reflected. "Sometimes it's better, as an activist, to not be such an extreme purist that you won't accept anything but the 100 percent purest form of what you want. That's a self-defeating strategy. You have to be willing to accept some compromise. Maybe you'll get 75 or 80 percent of what you want...that's better than not getting anything."

At last, on December 2, 1980, President Carter signed the Alaska Lands Act into law. Just in time. It turned out to be the single largest expansion of protected lands in United States history, more than doubling the size of the entire national parks system.

My dad smiled as he recalled the signing ceremony with the president. A picture of the signing still hangs in his office, perhaps as motivation or a symbol of hope for bipartisanship. The Alaska Coalition's job was done—they had a big celebration, shared hugs and thank-yous, and disbanded to go their separate ways. Alaskan Senator Mike Gravel, after his famous filibuster, was not re-elected.

At this point, you are probably, and rightfully, wondering: How does this lengthy backstory relate to climate activism? Well, I realized the four qualities that launched my dad's environmental career, listed below, are the same values he's tried to instill in my brother and me from when we were young. And they've helped me become not just a better environmentalist, but a better person.

So, take the time to sit down with your parents (or children, if you are the parents), to listen and learn.

- **Confidence in youth**
  - My dad "finessed" his way into the field immediately after college and never let his fear of being unqualified stop him. Young people can benefit from having the courage to think outside the box, learn as they go, specialize in one issue, know what to say (or when to shut up), elevate their own creative ideas, and bring a unique boldness and mischief to activism.

- **Optimism toward compromise**
  - The best way to be reasonable and rational is to facilitate compromise (or force it when necessary). The work of activism is so much more worthwhile when everyone remains "at ease and comfortable with accepting a final solution to an issue," as my dad put it. This outlook is similar to a lesson from one of my favorite law professors: Don't let the perfect be the enemy of the good.

- **Eagerness to tap into familiar identities**
  - These could be parental identities, best-friend-down-the-street identities, or any form of personal connections. Activism could mean enjoying a Saturday afternoon lunch with someone.

- **Integrity of a life by example**
  - Inspire habits in other people by practicing what you preach. My dad is proud of his quirky environmental habits: sabotaging thermostats to save energy,

installing money-saving solar panels on his house, driving an electric car, and producing very little landfill waste. Will these habits singlehandedly save the world? No. But that's not why he upholds them— he upholds them for the sake of personal integrity as an environmentalist. It's just a matter of being able to live with yourself in your habits!

Finally, I asked my dad if his environmental lifestyle ever felt like a sacrifice.

His answer surprised me. "I never really felt like I was giving up anything." In the glint of the hotel room's dim lighting, I saw my dad tear up slightly.

"I felt like I was doing what I love to do...and it was where my heart was. So, I may not have made as much money as some other professions might have, but I would make enough to be comfortable. [...] I think you find that it's not money that brings you satisfaction in life, but it's doing what you love and doing what has meaning to you that makes life satisfying and rewarding and happy."

"Thank you, Dad," I replied. It felt like I was thanking him for a lot more than our informal interview.

* * *

As my brother and I plan a trip to Alaska together, I can't help but appreciate that we'll be exploring the lands our dad helped protect.

And the more I think about his positive impact on Alaska, on the world of environmentalism, and on me as a person, the more my mind wanders back to the #NoFutureNoChildren pledge. Understanding the grim projections on climate change, it is so tempting to fall into that first camp and reject the notion of having kids altogether—I would be lying if I said I haven't thought about it.

But talking to my dad reminded me of that third camp, affirming that climate change is a multigenerational problem, and that on the scale of human survival, we could view having kids as raising a new generation of environmental warriors.

And if I'm able to instill even a fraction of my dad's passion in my own children, they will indeed be warriors.

That is hope enough for me.

CHAPTER 6

UNITY IN ECO-NOMICS

———

We reached the old wolf in time to watch a fierce green fire dying in her eyes. I realized then and have known ever since that there was something new to me in those eyes, something known only to her and to the mountain. I was young then and full of trigger-itch; I thought that because fewer wolves meant more deer, that no wolves would mean hunters' paradise. But after seeing the green fire die, I sensed that neither the wolf nor the mountain agreed with such a view.

—ALDO LEOPOLD

THE MOST DELICATE BALANCE

If there were ever a time the entire United States was collectively warned against upsetting the ecological balances of the natural world, it would be during the Dust Bowl of the 1930s.

All across the Great Plains of the United States (as well as parts of Canada and Mexico), unanchored soil eroded in the wind and turned into clouds of dust before the eyes of bewildered farmers. A combination of abnormally high temperatures, drought, and poor farming practices had degraded the soil itself into an airborne hazard. Farms had been deep-plowed with mechanized farm equipment and cleared of the native grasses that would otherwise protect the land from extreme erosion.

The picture was nothing short of apocalyptic: enormous plumes of darkened dust billowed into the air and settled over farmlands (they were called "black blizzards"), as if in the aftermath of a volcanic explosion, and dust-pneumonia killed farmers and their emaciated cattle alike. Crops failed to grow; soil failed to anchor them. When rain would finally arrive, it came in quick bursts that only worsened runoff. The ecological destruction was paralleled only by the magnitude of economic losses that followed. Unemployment skyrocketed, intensifying the effects of the Great Depression. A mass migration of 3.5 million people out of the Great Plains (1930-1940) turned out to be the largest the United States had experienced over a short time.[64] Hunger, poverty, and homelessness afflicted farm workers as well as white-collar and professional workers.

One farmer describes not only the "pitiful bareness" of fields, but the ghastly conditions of necessities such as her drinking water. When she dips out a bucket of water to carry to the henhouse, it "looks almost as if it were covered with a film of oil."

---

64 Donald Worster, *Dust Bowl: The Southern Plains in the 1930s* (Oxford: Oxford University Press, 2004), 49.

That farmer, who opted to stay behind with her husband on their twenty-eight-year-old farm in Oklahoma, wrote in a series of letters to her friend in Maryland:

Since I wrote to you, we have had several bad days of wind and dust. On the worst one recently, old sheets stretched over door and window openings, and sprayed with kerosene, quickly became black and helped a little to keep down the irritating dust in our living rooms. Nothing that you see or hear or read will be likely to exaggerate the physical discomfort or material losses due to these storms. Less emphasis is usually given to the mental effect, the confusion of mind resulting from the overthrow of all plans for improvement or normal farm work, and the difficulty of making other plans, even in a tentative way. [...] The pleasantest morning may be a prelude to an afternoon when the 'dust devils' all unite in one hideous onslaught.[65]

The Dust Bowl serves as a reminder that climatic changes can and will deliver drastic blows to food production and human well-being.

---

65 Caroline A. Henderson, "Letters from the Dust Bowl," *The Atlantic*, May 1936.

Though they suffered the worst effects of this ecological crisis, farmers should not be the scapegoats to blame. The error has been described by historians as a general lack of understanding toward the ecological impacts of farming techniques, which is in part due to the novelty of mechanized harvest machines. Also, in the wake of the Great Depression, so many banks had failed in the Plains states that farmers could not access the credit and capital they would have needed to invest in sustainable agricultural practices.[66] Just like in any just transition today, *incentivization* for farmers is key, and there was little to no incentivization given to them before the Dust Bowl.

Keeping these factors in mind, how is the Dust Bowl instructive on twenty-first century climate activism?

- **It is historical evidence of what extreme drought can—and will—look like in the United States.**

Any time I encounter people who discredit grassroots activists for being "too hyperbolic" on the effects of climate change, my mind returns to the Dust Bowl.

"Drought is the most pressing problem caused by climate change," comments Joseph Romm in *Nature*.[67] "It receives too little attention." You've heard the list of symptoms that intensify periods of drought. Shifting precipitation patterns.

---

66 John Landon-Lane, Hugh Rockoff, and Richard Steckel, "Droughts, Floods, and Financial Distress in the United States," *NBER Working Paper No. 15596* (December 2009): 6.

67 Joseph Romm, "The Next Dust Bowl," *Nature* 478 (October 2011): 450.

Extreme floods and runoff. Evaporation and soil drying. Earlier snowmelt. All of these, combined with natural El Niño-La Niña variation, will contribute to what Romm calls "desertification." Well, he used to call it that, before a reader pointed out that many deserts are still high in biodiversity. "Dust-bowlification" is the term he settled on instead, sufficiently accurate and vivid for Americans who still perceive climate change as a far-away problem. And in his eerily titled piece "The Next Dust Bowl," Romm concludes that such arid conditions will likely arise again.

- **It involved the "uprooting" of early climate refugees.**

Through my grassroots lens, the Dust Bowl illustrates how climate refugees (like the migrant "Okies") are forced to abandon the legacy they would otherwise pass on to their children. Even in the most literal sense, neither grass nor roots remained intact in the farmlands that once sustained their livelihood.

Generationally, only older members of the silent generation (1928–1945) and earlier would remember growing up during the Dust Bowl, and few storytellers remain among them. However, an interesting trend can be observed in polling their climate beliefs: Silent generation Democrats are actually *more* convinced global warming is happening than are millennial Democrats.[68] Perhaps growing up in an era closer to the Dust Bowl, and witnessing the science and

---

68 Matthew Ballew et al., "Do Younger Generations Care More about Global Warming?" *Yale Program on Climate Change Communication*, June 11, 2019.

policy advancements since then, offers a new perspective on climate events.

- **Unconventional activists documented the crisis through photography and the arts.**

If there were a Dust Bowl activist at the time, perhaps it would be Dorothea Lange, the photographer who captured most of the famous textbook images we associate with the time period (including her iconic photograph of a concerned migrant mother, which reveals the intergenerational nature of the exodus). Additionally, author John Steinbeck documented the Dust Bowl in *The Grapes of Wrath,* and folk singer Woody Guthrie traveled alongside migrants and emulated their music as he sang about hardship and social injustice in songs such as "This Land is Your Land." These were our early climate storytellers.

- **Farmers acknowledged the success of Federal programs.**

President Roosevelt quickly deployed federal aid programs under his New Deal, such as the Soil Erosion Service (to help farmers implement terracing, crop rotation, contour farming, etc. to control erosion) and the Federal Surplus Relief Corporation (to regulate surpluses, divert resources to relief organizations, and feed and clothe the needy). Programs like these expanded the role of government in land conservation, which proved to be an important and necessary outcome of the disaster.

"That there was anything at all to harvest we attribute to the new planting methods encouraged by the Soil Erosion

Control service," writes farmer Caroline A. Henderson in her letter to a friend.[69] I was surprised by her willingness to openly defend federal involvement:

> *The plan has been proposed and carried through here as a matter of public policy for the welfare of all without reproach or humiliation to anyone. [...] If the severe critics of all who in any way join in government plans for the saving of homes and the restoration of farms to a productive basis could only understand how vital a human problem is here considered, possibly their censures might be less bitter and scornful.*

Businessmen and farmers alike recognized that federal wage payment and projects saved the territory from abandonment. However, these were all implemented through continuous dialogue and partnerships with the farmers; "individual conferences, to suit the farm and the farmer."

Climate solutions should be implemented with the same mindset.

* * *

And so, with the Dust Bowl's reminder of the dangers of *unsustainability*—realizing monetary prosperity depends

---

69 Henderson, "Letters from the Dust Bowl."

entirely on the health of the natural world—we continue searching for unity in modern *Eco*-nomics.

(Eco-nomics is a quaint abbreviation for ecosystem-centered economics.)

Keeping economics ecosystem-centered is a challenge in and of itself:

- It is prudent in purely economic terms for corporations, as rational self-interested actors, to avoid climate action. They'd instead minimize their personal action, treat the climate as a public good, and "free ride" on the diffuse benefits of other people's climate commitments.
- The social cost of carbon is often excluded from cost-benefit analyses.
- Profits are prioritized; ecosystem health comes secondarily.

However, Americans have enough economic goals in common with one another that unity in Eco-nomics may be possible.

Putting aside the "shrill divisiveness" of media and politics, American voters have surprisingly consistent visions of what they want for their children's futures, explains sustainability expert Paul Hawken. A cleaner environment, safer communities, better schools, lower taxes, greater economic security, more effective government, strengthened family support, and well-paying jobs, are among the nearly indisputable commonalities we share.[70] In this regard, we're all the same. Each goal can be fulfilled if we emphasize ecosystem capital.

We have enough values in common that the public and private sector might be able to come together to fulfill those rights in meaningful partnerships.

To delve deeper into what that means, we'll start by examining Eco-nomics on a conceptual scale.

And that brings us to Spaceship Earth.

A SINKING SHIP

There is a popular economic analogy called "Spaceship Earth," which likens our planet to exactly that: a spaceship stocked with finite resources, shared by all of humankind, hurtling through space beyond the control of its inhabitants. We are Team Human.

Economist Barbara Ward first came up with the term in 1966, and it was popularized by Buckminster Fuller.[71] It parallels a much darker concept nicknamed "lifeboat ethics," or "Lifeboat Earth," proposing that the Earth can only support a limited number of people and requires us to make

---

70 Paul Hawken, Amory Lovins, and L. Hunter Lovins, *Natural Capitalism: Creating the Next Industrial Revolution* (Boston: Little, Brown and Co., 1999), 322.

71 Adam Roth, "Sustainability: The Launch of Spaceship Earth," *Nature* 527 (November 2015): 443-445.

survival calls based on that.[72] (I refuse to entertain the fields of eugenics or eco-fascism in this book, so I will continue the transportation analogy under the assumption that there is no "overboard.")

* * *

In many ways, it is fitting to say we live on a boat or a spaceship...because there is nowhere else for us to go.

(To the Elon Musk generation: Chances are, we'd spend most of our time on Mars missing Earth.)

Scientists continue to scan the fringes beyond our solar system for exoplanets that might support life. Astrobiology, the study of life in the universe based on what we know about life on Earth, is without a doubt a fascinating discipline (often studied in the remote hills of Antarctica to mimic the possible environments of Earth-like planets). But the idea of a utopian Earth-like travel destination, close by and ready for passengers within the next century of our population and climate peril, is equally as unviable as it is exciting.

And even if the destination and technology existed, could we comfortably say we did everything we could to save Spaceship Earth before abandoning ship?

---

72 Roderick Frazier Nash, ed., *American Environmentalism: Readings in Conservation History, Third Edition* (McGraw-Hill, 1990), 237.

Ward and Fuller's concept of "Spaceship Earth" was part of a broader shift in the 1960s–70s for human beings to think of ourselves as global citizens.

The publication of the Apollo 8 crew's famous photograph *Earthrise* (1968) defined, without words, the essence of global citizenship.[73] It captured an image of the shadowed Earth from lunar orbit to be shared with the world on Christmas Eve. This small, fragile planet, a bold speck of blue suspended in the cosmos, is all that is keeping us alive. We are its passengers.

At the same time, I think imagining our planet as a boat, spaceship, or other form of enclosed transportation gives us the false sense of security that we are somehow "at the wheel," steering and controlling the vessel in the arbitrary direction of progress. All life on Earth is at the whim of the planet's natural fluxes. And any changes humans decide to make to the balance of those fluxes—whether backlogging the carbon cycle through emissions and deforestation, tainting the water cycle with sulfur dioxide, or disrupting the nutrient cycle by plowing away topsoil and turning a drought into a Dust Bowl—will ultimately be what "steers" the planet one step closer to prosperity or collapse.

Economic growth must proceed with according caution on Spaceship Earth. Our stockpile of resources is limited by factors of *time*; fossil fuels pressed over time from the geological remains of ancient organisms, old growth forests and peat bogs sequestering unimaginable amounts of

---

73   William Anders, *Earthrise*, 1968, photograph, NASA website.

carbon over the centuries, or one-of-a-kind species evolved over hundreds of thousands of years only to be pushed to the brink of extinction. Researchers have used computer models to generate hundreds of scenarios simulating *growth* in human society…and nearly all of them follow a pattern of "exponential growth of population and capital, followed by collapse."[74] Not just the worst-case scenario—the majority of them. Biology too is limited by space and time; unrestrained growth is not possible without that eventual collapse.

Maybe that's the hole in the side of Lifeboat Earth.

Much of it comes down not to the fact that we're consuming, but the *way* we're consuming.

In a problem that economists have named the "tragedy of the commons," each individual in a group is incentivized to deplete resources shared by that group, even if it means damaging consequences for all.[75] For example, if twenty people fish at the same pond every day, one of them might arrive early with a net and overfish, so he has more to sell, depleting the resource for all the other fishermen. He is offered no incentive to leave the fish in the pond—his only incentive is to fish more for himself. In this situation, the shared resource is overused, just like in environmental challenges such as overgrazing, deforestation, air pollution, and, notably, global climate change. An *unrestricted commons*, such as an

---

74   Nash, *American Environmentalism*, 239.

75   Jonathan B. Wiener, "The Tragedy of the Uncommons: On the Politics of Apocalypse," *Global Policy* 7, supp. no. 1 (May 2016): 67.

economy in which greenhouse gases are completely unregulated and ignored in cost analyses, leads to ruin.

Lifeboat Earth takes on water.

On top of the tragedy of the commons problem is the problem of consumer culture. All generations are familiar with shopping sprees and the culture of compulsive buying. Economist Victor Lebow summarized it best over sixty years ago:

Our enormously productive economy demands that we make consumption our way of life, that we convert the buying and use of goods into rituals, that we seek our spiritual satisfactions, our ego satisfactions, in consumption. [...] We need things consumed, burned up, worn out, replaced, and discarded at an ever-increasing pace.[76]

This picture of our economy is linear. It is throwaway. And, on top of environmental stress, its disposable nature leads to economic inequality.

Is there a way for us, as activists, to instead fight for *smart growth*—equitable growth—that might steer nature's course away from collapse?

---

76   Victor Lebow, "Price Competition in 1955," *Journal of Retailing* 31, no. 1 (Spring 1955): 3.

One innovative, grassroots idea is a circular economy. A circular economy involves distributing goods strategically to reduce unnecessary waste and the environmental costs of production. This could mean complex initiatives all along the supply chain to make sure every usable "by-product" from a factory is sent off to fulfill another purpose, or simpler initiatives like composting in elementary schools or Bring-Your-Own-Bag shopping.

Up to 40 percent of food is wasted in the United States and condemned to sit in a landfill releasing greenhouse gases.[77] For that frustrating reason, even the small interventions on food waste make a big difference to me, morally and climatically. (You know those trays of doughnuts at 7-11 that sit by the counter tantalizingly only to be tossed at the end of the day? Heartbreaking, and definitely not even the worst example of food waste. Regardless of environmental or political views, I think most people would rather see those carts of doughnuts delivered to homeless shelters than thrown in the garbage).

The life cycle of plastic is no less disappointing, as islands of it circulate in the ocean and accumulate in the digestive tracts of marine life. You may have heard the environmental adage, "Recycling is a symptom of disposability," and it's important to make that distinction in Eco-nomics.

---

77 "Food Waste FAQs," USDA.

Regardless of what we've been told about recycling, one-third of plastic waste globally is *not* collected or managed.[78] Plastic bottle companies have no problem endorsing recycling left and right; it helps them sell more bottles! (Nestlé and other packagers were careful to endorse *Keep America Beautiful* ad campaigns in the late twentieth century to ensure consumers still bought plastic bottles, just with the added moral alleviation of throwing them in a blue bin.) When picking your battles as an activist, I would advise moving beyond recycling and onto the larger root issue of wastefulness.

A circular economy means putting every product to good use (which *helps* profits), giving materials a life cycle beyond a landfill, and distributing resources to alleviate poverty and inequality. Harmoniously round, like a doughnut.

Several Eco-nomic case studies prove this kind of sustainable economy isn't too far-fetched or costly. The economy and the environment do not have to be in battle with each other.

In Europe, timber was heavily used in pretty much every industrial sector (fuel, furniture, construction, etc.) through the 1900s, when there was scarcely any forested area left on the entire continent. However, agro-technological innovations such as motorization, better drainage, and mass irrigation enabled farmers to produce the same volume of food

---

78 Walter R. Stahel, "The Circular Economy," *Nature* 531, no. 7595 (March 2016): 435.

with much less cropland, allowing areas for reforestation without decreasing industry yields.[79]

In a tragedy of the commons example, air pollution in the United States and many other countries has dramatically declined for almost fifty years, even as economies grew.[80]

States have benefitted from doubly designating conservation areas as ecotourism hotspots. North Carolina, especially, attracts a significant amount of state revenue from hopeful red wolf spotters alone, traveling to the state for that purpose. The growth of the multi-million-dollar ecotourism industry depends on conservation.

How, then, does growth intersect with climate change?

THE CASE FOR ECO-NOMICS

In one of my favorite analogies thus far, Roderick Frazier Nash imagines population and economic growth in the face of climate change like a man in free fall off the side of a building.[81]

Toward the beginning of his fall, he looks around him and considers grabbing onto a nearby ledge to slow his fall.

---

79 Leigh Phillips, "The Degrowth Delusion," openDemocracy, last modified August 30, 2019.

80 Wiener, "The Tragedy of the Uncommons," 68.

81 Nash, *American Environmentalism,* 239.

The man ultimately resolves against it, worried he'd fracture a wrist or bruise an arm.

Breaking my fall wouldn't be worth the personal injury, he decides.

But with every additional story he falls, he accelerates, plummeting faster and faster toward the ground.

Should he change his mind and decide to grab onto a ledge, it becomes nearly impossible to do so the longer he falls in indecision.

Finally, the man passes a certain point in his descent and realizes a collision with the ground looks to be a far worse fate than a broken arm. But it's already too late to slow his fall.

This is the plight of generational climate (in)action: Policymakers waffle back and forth on whether to cut back on fossil fuels when it might mean risking a broken arm for the economy.

"Moreover, most of the benefits would go to non-Americans who haven't even been born yet," clarifies Columbia Law professor Jedediah Purdy, explaining rather pessimistically that nations won't hesitate to act in their self-interest and, in the classic tragedy of the commons scenario, sell out their descendants.

In some ways, this is the worse problem. Countries can get together to solve shared problems, though often with difficulty, because their governments can all come to the same table. If we imagined generations, however, as if they were negotiators in climate talks, we would discover that the only one actually present at the table is always the present generation—that one that will bear all the costs of doing something about the problem, and receive almost none of the benefits.[82]

So, policymakers hold off on committing to binding agreements. (And I thought teenagers were stereotyped to be the procrastinators?) The United States first avoids setting hard numerical emissions goals in the Kyoto Protocol, then shirks its responsibility to even nominally remain in the Paris Accords under President Trump.

Meanwhile, climate change does not hold off.

What I find most interesting about this irreversible, Dust Bowl-level planetary change on our horizon is how it upholds alongside the definition of conservatism, as observed in the *Bulletin of Atomic Scientists*:

---

82   Jedediah Purdy, *After Nature: A Politics for the Anthropocene* (Cambridge: Harvard University Press, 2015), 247.

Usually we think of conservative action as one of no interference on current practices. Change is regarded as nonconservative action, and the old-fashioned conservative advises us to take no such positive action until we have made exhaustive studies of the phenomena involved. But when human survival is at stake, is clinging to the status quo conservative?[83]

Conservatism should mean *resisting that change* (climate change) by any means necessary, especially considering that the rise of tropical diseases, food shortages, soil degradation, and mass migrations resulting from climate change inaction down the road would require unprecedented levels of government involvement. Think of the Dust Bowl relief programs on a national scale.

In one study, Republicans read climate literature and were then shown policy solutions such as taxes and government regulation; 22 percent reported they believed what they read in the scientific statement. However, when a free-market solution was offered instead, all of a sudden 55 percent of Republicans agreed with the scientific statement.[84]

---

83 Garrett Hardin, "Limits to Growth—Two Views: We Live on a Spaceship," *Bulletin of the Atomic Scientists* 28, no. 9 (November 1972): 24

84 Troy H. Campbell and Aaron C. Kay, "Solution aversion: On the relation between ideology and motivated disbelief." *Journal of Personality and Social Psychology 107, no. 5 (2014):* 809–824.

Liberals should be mindful of communicating multifaceted solutions, including community-based environmental management, sustainability incentives in business or agriculture, direct support for farmers, and investments in Green Tech, which go beyond solely touting government regulation. Studies have shown the urban-rural divide has very little to do with people's level of care for the environment (rural stakeholders have a strong sense of identity and place tied to the environment) or knowledge on environmental issues—it instead appears to be a function of their level of trust in the federal government.[85] Believe it or not, rural Midwesterners' support for taking climate action jumped over 20 percent when it was explicitly connected to also helping farmers.[86]

Overall, rural residents play a huge role in elections and offer valuable insights into land management and the realities of farming.

We cannot leave them behind in our fight to save the climate.

Liberal or conservative, rural or urban, old or young, how do we propose a solution that *all* of us can fight for in the grassroots?

---

85   Robert Bonnie, Emily Pechar Diamond, and Elizabeth Rowe, "Understanding Rural Attitudes Toward the Environment and Conservation in America," *The Nicholas Institute for Environmental Policy Solutions*, report, March 2020.

86   Emily Diamond, Robert Bonnie, and Elizabeth Rowe, "Rural Attitudes on Climate Change: Lessons from National and Midwest Polling and Focus Groups," report (in press), 2020.

The answer is not proposing that each of us, as individuals, try harder to "Save the Earth" through lifestyle choices alone.

The 2020 coronavirus outbreak debunked that comfortable option once and for all. The outbreak forced families across the globe to stay quarantined indoors, severely limiting economic activity to the point of recession and a near shutdown on all air travel. In the end, the projected 5.5 percent reduction in carbon emissions *still* falls short of the percentage needed to avoid the worst of the IPCC's warming scenarios—that would require a drop of 7.6 percent every year for the next decade.[87]

Even if we were able to live a quarantine lifestyle every day for the next ten to twenty years (imagine that), families "cutting back" remains fruitless so long as unregulated corporate polluters continue their emissions. Frankly, it's not fair to all of us, who are simply told to take shorter showers and turn off the lights while corporations pay nothing for emitting the greenhouse gases that condemn us.

FOLLOW THE MONEY: PRICING THE ENVIRONMENT
One thing most people in the United States support is a strong economy and a wide availability of jobs. Gen Z differs from its predecessors in the sense that we pursue idea-based jobs, rooted in postindustrial creative industries, whereas

---

87 Melody Shreiber, "The Coronavirus and the Limits of Individual Climate Action," *The New Republic*, last modified April 27, 2020.

older generations grew up on an economy that was distinctly product-based.

A lot of times we see older Americans express a deep need to defend certain product-based or extractive industries, such as steel, coal, oil, and chemical manufacturing because it's what supported them in their families or their hometowns growing up. Even my mom grew up in Pittsburgh, an industrial but very welcoming steel mill town. I think of hometowns like hers before shunning any steel, coal, or oil loyalists, and I instead emphasize how important a just and equitable transition is for the people whose economic prosperity currently depends on an extractive product.

A consensus I'm starting to hear as I am talking to experts is that a just transition sometimes means paying out whatever they're owed to make a green transition. Based on the palatable doctrine of "Follow the Money," sometimes negotiations are much shorter when there is a reasonable price tag involved—high transaction costs tend to deter collective action.[88] Side payments and easy roadmaps tend to move partnerships along.

For example, even the chemical giant Dupont reversed their stubborn position on CFCs as soon as they heard readily-available alternatives to aerosols existed—and it would make them money to switch. Just like that, Dupont went "full send" (as my generation would say) in favor of the Montreal Protocol, which helped restore the ozone layer. And because

---

88 Wiener, "The Tragedy of the Uncommons," 68.

the economy and the environment are so profoundly inter-connected, the payoffs will be twofold.

As the father of Earth Day, Senator Gaylord Nelson, put it,

"The economy is a wholly owned subsidiary of the environment."[89]

One of the benefits of quantifying the value of ecosystem services is that it grants environmentalists a long-lost power to speak on a practical level with economists, many of whom simply don't consider natural spaces to have any inherent worth outside of food or production for humans. One of my professors even mentioned that the only climate solution people in positions of power might receive open-mindedly would be one in which the rich keep all their wealth or get richer. Navigating this reality is bound to be challenging, especially for scrappy Gen Zers and millennials wishing to challenge older, wealthier, and more experienced CEOs and executives.

In other words, it's difficult to talk about divestment from fossil fuels with the person who owns your job. Or with the people who own your university.

That's pretty close to what students did during halftime of the Yale-Harvard rivalry football game of 2019, when roughly seventy climate-conscious students staged a protest in the

---

89 NPR Soundbite (2000), In "Earth Day Founder Gaylord Nelson Dies," *NPR Morning Edition*, radio show, July 4, 2005.

middle of the field. Some held banners, some held megaphones, and they all held a grudge against the trustees and executives of their universities who had dodged the topic of divestment for too long.

The students had strategically planned to disrupt a game they knew *thousands of alumni and donors* were bound to be watching. Within minutes, hundreds of parents and spectators rushed onto the field to join them in a rather moving, adrenaline-packed gathering. Protestors refused to leave the field. Proud parents snapped pictures of their kids receiving disorderly conduct summons from the police. Though some spectators were annoyed ("Drag them off the field!"), the mood was joyous throughout the game's delay of nearly an hour.

If divestment were a moral issue, or an issue of whether climate change is happening, the outcry of promising students should have swayed their institutions' fossil fuel funders. However, divestment proves to be an economic issue that will continue to depend on the price of clean energy versus fossil fuels.

It's a bit more challenging to convince policymakers to price greenhouse gases (from fossil fuels) because they don't resemble traditional pollutants—they're not toxic. They don't take the form of river sludge or visible plumes of dust. Many are natural, diffuse, and are exhaled quite innocently by living creatures. Unlike prior generations' successes fighting for Superfund cleanups or against Clean Water violations, the environmental justice damages of climate change are easier for policymakers to brush off. *Hurricanes? Fires? Hog lagoon overflow? Let's view these as isolated events and disconnect them from corporate emissions.* In fact, it's much, much easier to maintain that disconnect when lobbyists carefully urge policymakers to make the wrong kinds of investments—to follow the wrong kinds of money.

However, the "Follow the Money" paradigm can be redefined in a way that generates unity and provides a fair case for sustainability in the long term. We must conserve natural resources, like forests and fisheries, simply because we *cannot afford to squander limited natural resource capital.* If we overharvest, the product is gone forever, for everyone. The ancient forest is clear-cut. The animal is extinct. The permafrost carbon sink is emptied; it's already warming the planet. And our next generations will grow up picking at the scraps of exploited industries.

AN ECONOMY OF IDEAS

According to Rohin Shahi, author of *The Z Factor*, Gen Zers are socially conscious individuals who thrive on ideas. It is fitting that the Green New Deal (and Alexandria Ocasio-Cortez) epitomize our generation's economy of ideas.

The Green New Deal (GND) legislation itself is often criticized as being an idealistic goal that "doesn't really do anything." Well, in a sense it's true. The legislation wasn't written to "do" anything in meticulous detail so much as it was intended to serve as a vision, or a *framework,* for future plans. It's a broad commitment—an idea, if you will—designed to leave room for innovation and job creation. Once passed, states will have a lot of agency to determine their tangible policy approaches to fulfilling the goals of the GND. Overall, a challenge for my generation moving forward will be balancing ideology and practice when it comes to climate change solutions.

THE CAPACITY OF A COALITION

For my final exploration into the world of Eco-nomics between generations, I enjoyed a lunch conversation with Francis Grant-Suttie during which we discussed the professional side of the environmental community.

Francis is a seasoned environmental veteran on the fronts of land conservation and climate change. He has worked for the World Resources Institute, World Wildlife Fund (WWF), National Audubon Society, and serves on the board for the Chesapeake & Ohio Canal Trust. He has faced a number of diverse environmental challenges in his career. One of the reasons Francis has been so successful is that he is a coalition builder—as well as a frontline advocate and elite negotiator.

Francis is also a natural people-person. I even see it in our interview, as he tells engaging stories, eyes twinkling, and two hours have passed before I am even aware of it.

Interestingly, Francis spent most of his childhood away from people. Born in Zimbabwe (then Rhodesia), he grew up in the wilderness twenty miles out from the main city, Harare. "I grew up with wildlife only around me, and I also grew up with the concept of wildness," he explained to me. As a kid, his mother would sometimes give him a big piece of jerky and he would eat it slowly as his only food for two or three days, as he set out every day in shorts and sandals. Living out in "the middle of nowhere," far from the city, granted Francis a healthy appreciation for nature that he still considers intrinsic to who he is as a person. Though it sometimes lay dormant as he journeyed into the more structured institutions of boarding school in England and college in the United States, his childhood experiences in nature formed the foundations of his environmentalism.

Out of college, he first began working for the World Resources Institute, helping to create its corporate program, which entailed learning how to build relationships. From that early fresh-out-of-college age, Francis learned an extremely valuable skill in eco-communication: strategically engaging with corporations.

He then accepted a position in Washington, D.C., as the head of corporate fundraising for World Wildlife Fund, one of the largest environmental organizations in the world.

Negotiation was never easy. "Follow the money" is the unfortunate but realistic motto of many business entities, we agreed, where ideological (or moralizing) negotiation alone falls short.

However, after working for a couple of years, Francis realized the corporate fundraising side of things was remarkably easy. It seemed everyone wanted to buy a relationship with WWF. In the environmental field, the organization is what we call a "BINGO," or a big international non-governmental organization. WWF was the biggest BINGO in the business. Some partnerships are well-intentioned but verged on public relations greenwashing. So, Francis wanted to leverage these relationships with the goal of changing corporate behavior *outside* of the realm of fundraising.

Francis then approached the president of WWF and suggested an alternative approach to corporate fundraising. He envisioned a new position for WWF in the worldwide program policy arena, in which their relationships with global companies would actually be trying to affect policies and practices in the field and on the ground. Thus, the Private Sector Initiatives program was created. He often found he would be orchestrating projects targeting habitat protection, bringing together Greenpeace and activist organizations with government and hundreds of corporations, merging different groups of stakeholders to negotiate environmental protection. Coalitions were crucial. "It was always a 'we,'" Francis remarked.

He began working with companies across many sectors (but with an emphasis on the extractive resource industries like oil and gas, mining, and forestry) to examine the impacts of industry on climate change, biodiversity, toxic contamination, local communities, and the environment...in spite of negative backlash, and in spite of the fact that these conversations were considered radically progressive even in the 1990s, when the idea of sustainability was just getting off the ground.

Francis's idea soon became a global initiative.

And corporations often aligned themselves with the goals of WWF. Even after the tensions of the Kyoto Protocol of 1997 (after which America was viewed as completely opposed to greenhouse gas reductions), Francis got one hundred companies to sign a public statement in the *Asian Wall Street Journal* committing to tackling the impacts of climate change. Subsequently, Francis set up a new program, Climate Savers, enlisting major corporations to commit to absolute reductions in their GHG emissions worldwide, many of whom had signed the original Kyoto document—no small victory in the Kyoto aftermath.

He continued to lead negotiations internationally, but he ensured everyone had a seat at the table in them—indigenous and impacted peoples, and environmental groups at all levels, along with hundreds of boots-on-the-ground, demonstration-inclined activist groups, bolstered in their missions by social media in negotiating with governments, corporations, and the international financial industry. Francis was a coalition builder. WWF teams and all its partners were ready to stare down corporations together. In many cases, this required full-fledged public campaigning using all the skills and tactics throughout the environmental community.

How do you challenge some of the most powerful, well-financed corporations in the world? Or engage with a corporate group that goes against the very mission of WWF?

Francis had a few stories to share.

The first involved Cairn Energy, a UK-based oil and gas company that wanted to drill in the Terai Arc for oil in the most productive agricultural region of Nepal. Cairn would be drilling between and in watersheds, Francis explained. Bad news for the environment. So, he spent weeks in Nepal gathering information by listening to the needs and concerns of farmers, villages, and communities, none of whom would benefit from Cairn's environmental destruction.

When the time came for the final negotiation with Cairn, Francis was straightforward. "You don't wanna do this." He spoke not only for WWF but for the *people* with whom he'd spent the past several weeks. In the end, they stopped the development. Francis navigated this so successfully by recognizing that local grassroots movements and high-level organizations *do* interact—and they empower each other more than we realize.

In another story, Francis helped coordinate a victory in South America. Boise Cascade, a wood product company based in Idaho, proposed to build the largest pulp mill (known as the Cascada project) adjacent to a fishing town in Puerto Montt, Chile. The project would be massively destructive toward Chile's ancient forest (and major forestry program), and this would be the last chance to save them. So, after forming a coalition of local groups, indigenous people, and Greenpeace, Francis was ready to unleash their combined power through WWF and give Cascade a hard "NO."

The negotiations took place in Boise, Idaho. Greenpeace demonstrated on the streets outside of the Boise Cascade headquarters while Francis was up in the boardroom urging them to abandon the pulp mill project—quite literally creating pressure from multiple levels. The outcome was a success—Cascade pulled out of the project. (Their cited reason was that pulp prices went down, but the real reason was the unimaginable pressure these stakeholders put on them.)

The takeaway? The environmental community work collectively to achieve results and never work alone.

Francis brought activism and social responsibility into the corporate picture. It was rare to have an "elite negotiator" approach that goal by working closely with the Greenpeaces and Rainforest Action Networks of the world. But it was valuable—he merged the goals of promoting grassroots activism and trying to address corporate responsibility. "I had one foot in both camps," he recalls. "And it was perfect, in the sense that you could have common ground and be constructive."

THE CHALLENGES OF COMMON GROUND

Before talking to Francis, I repeated the phrase "common ground" with a naive sense of optimism, believing that enough constructive back-and-forth with any entity would end in compromise. This is not always the case. For instance, he engaged oil companies in the most vulnerable stretches of the Amazon and elsewhere in some of the most biodiverse and vulnerable regions in the world, trying to get them to develop a set of best practices to follow while extracting oil—one that would not harm indigenous people and their land. It proved to be impossible. The reason, he told me, was that there *are* no best practices for an extractive industry on indigenous land.

It was also difficult to negotiate with an industry that was so lucrative and refused to compromise profits. In most cases, the coalitions would fight to stop the projects directly. These were considered "No-Go Zones," where oil extraction and the accumulated impacts from pipelines destroyed habitat and impacted sustainable livelihood, but ultimately contributed to climate change.

Other challenges lie in negotiating the best means of "conservation" itself. A large portion of WWF's work is on the ground, going out into the field, working in villages, or setting up national parks (they've put together over 600 national park centers). But the mission of environmental conservation is evolving into something more complicated in the face of climate change. "Just because you have a national park doesn't mean you're saving actually anything; it just means it's a designation," Francis informs me. The central question at WWF, and most prominent NGOs, is translational: How do we really protect the planet at large?

The "purist" argument is lofty but tempting: Simply double—or triple—the size of all protected areas. Unfortunately, this type of place-based conservation falls short in several regards. For example, doubling or tripling the size of all protected areas doesn't mean you're addressing the root-level crises of unrestrained global greenhouse emissions or global toxic contaminants. Nor does a mere designation factor in the element of *people* and their needs. It was a question that always ran through Francis's mind. "How do you protect nature [...] and figure out how all these people are going to survive?" Here lies an issue at the heart of environmentalism: the challenge of preserving the beauty of a landscape or ecosystem without denying people food, shelter, resources, and basic economic sustenance.

I learned from Francis that it's impossible to address this challenge, or any challenge, without effective communication.

Step one is to bring people information, using the right language. Step two is to develop a relationship with them. The best example of this is a story Francis told me about protecting a strip of land with National Audubon Society in the southeast quadrant of South Carolina. The region is largely made up of landowners who have worked the land for many generations; it remains virtually unchanged since the Civil War. The landowners who lived there, he recalls, spoke of the war as if it were recent, to the point where it was inexorable from their culture.

The South Carolina Audubon was creative in using land-based tools—especially negotiating conservation easements with the landowners. (Agreement in which property is protected by a land trust.) In addition to listing the tax benefits and economic returns to the land, Audubon was adept in persuading owners to somehow acknowledge the ideological value of preserving land, using words like "legacy." The key issue was preserving land for future generations that allowed the legacy of landowners to perpetuate for their descendants. This tactic worked, and the team was highly successful in locking up large tracts of land under conservation easements. Francis, at the time, was the vice president in charge of the Atlantic Flyway.

At the same time, Francis advised me to be prepared to defend social and environmental justice—know what makes your challengers tick. Put in the work and research relevant news, stock prices, and political developments. Form coalitions with local indigenous groups, activists, professionals, and even unlikely allies, to strive toward that point of justice. All this adds up to preserving sustainable livelihoods that are a key feature of protecting the planet from climate change and all the other environmental impacts we are witnessing worldwide.

This is the heart of environmental diplomacy.

* * *

I thanked Francis for speaking with me, and he told me he is writing a book himself about peace. It is aptly titled, "Bits and Peaces." In addition to finding it in people and in nature, environmental diplomacy, in a sense, has taught him tranquility.

"[There are times when] everything is quiet...But then there are times when peace flourishes, whether it's in your own mind...or when you create [it]."

CHAPTER 7

SAVING STEWARDSHIP: LINKING RELIGION AND ENVIRONMENTALISM

The indescribable innocence and beneficence of Nature—of sun and wind and rain, of summer and winter—such health, such cheer, they afford forever! and such sympathy have they ever with our race, that all Nature would be affected, and the sun's brightness fade, and the winds would sigh humanely, and the clouds rain tears, and the woods shed their leaves and put on mourning in midsummer, if any man should ever for a just cause grieve. Shall I not have intelligence with the earth? Am I not partly leaves and vegetable mould myself?

—HENRY DAVID THOREAU

THE FIERCEST NEGOTIATORS

I asked Francis-Grant Suttie, who had spent a large portion of his life working on international partnerships in World

Wildlife Fund, to tell me more about the challenges of effective negotiation.

"Some of the toughest negotiators I've ever, *ever* been with, across the table, in any company . . ," he told me, "were nuns."

It was amusing to hear, not because I doubted the eloquence or morality of nuns themselves, but because I couldn't help but conjure the mental image of an impassioned, robe-clad nun slamming her fist on the table in a stubborn environmental ultimatum. Why were nuns, of all people, taking such a big stand against environmental destruction?

His answer was surprisingly simple. He told me there was no middle ground for them; no ifs, ands, or buts. When you're messing with creation, you're messing with God.

Is it that simple? This causes us to wonder, is there hope for an evangelical consensus on taking practical measures to protect God's creation? It turns out *stewardship* might be the very word that draws together generations and political parties—religious, atheist-agnostic, or anywhere in between—in the footsteps of the nuns.

STEWARDSHIP IN SCRIPTURE
In the Bible, humans are called to be stewards of the Earth.

To be a "steward" means to be "a person whose responsibility it is to take care of something."[90]

Once again, there is power in the simplicity and universality of a word's definition. "Steward" is an active word, doubling as a noun and a verb, that points to duty and responsibility. Climate activists and evangelicals share that strong sense of duty in common, even if it is perceived to be in service of different goals.

In fact, experimental data suggest crafting messages around stewardship and protecting God's creation can help turn environmental protection into a "mainstream" issue among Christians. As soon as environmental stewardship becomes a moral and religious issue—and even a social norm—Christians in the United States "increase their own pro-environmental and climate change beliefs."[91]

In this chapter, we'll look briefly at the concept of stewardship as it appears in the Christian ethic specifically (as Christianity is seen to be the religion that most correlates to climate denialism in the United States). Approximately 70 percent of the United States population identifies as Christian.[92]

---

90 *New Oxford American Dictionary* (digital), American English ed., s.v. "steward."

91 Matthew H. Goldberg et al., "Engaging Christians in the Issue of Climate Change," *Yale Program on Climate Change Communication*, July 12, 2019

92 Ibid.

Whether or not you are religious or spiritual, I hope the pieces of this chapter demonstrate how much room there is for unity between Christians and climate defenders.

Challenge number one.

Does Scripture undermine environmental protection?

Genesis 1:28 is a popular starting point:

> [28] "And God blessed them. And God said to them, 'Be fruitful and multiply and fill the earth and subdue it, and have dominion over the fish of the sea and over the birds of the heavens and over every living thing that moves on the earth.'"[93]

This line of scripture, in particular, leaves behind one of the most empowering and confusing instruction manuals for humankind.

At a first glance, it might seem that humans are told to rule the Earth. Some people read this line of scripture as a free pass for humans to exploit the Earth's natural resources as they see fit, exempt from the moralizing concerns of environmentalists. After all, shouldn't words like "dominion" and "subdue" indicate maybe we're being a little too sensitive toward the environmental crisis?

---

93   English Standard Version (ESV).

As it turns out, "dominion" is often misread in that way. Dominion does not mean senseless rule. Instead, dominion means responsible leadership, or stewardship, which is backed up by Biblical and translational evidence. Scholar Calvin DeWitt carves "dominion" (stewardship) into three tenets:

- **Earthkeeping**: In Genesis 2:15, the Hebrew words *abad* and *shamar* can be read as "to serve and keep nature in dynamic integrity."[94] Whether by budgeting carbon or preserving biodiversity, environmental policies serve that same goal of keeping nature's balance.
- **Fruitfulness**: In Genesis 1, above, God gives Adam the right to be bountiful in his habitat. DeWitt points out God gives the same right to Creation, not just humanity, elsewhere in the passage.[95]
- **The Sabbath**: In both the Hebrew and Christian traditions, the Sabbath represents the rejuvenation and restoration of life. Every seventh year, the land is allowed to rest. One-seventh of the land is left fallow. The Sabbath calls for moderation and balance—not overexploitation. In many translations, "subdue" is written as "replenish and subdue," a pairing that argues for the circular concept of sustainability.

---

94 Kyle S. Van Houtan and Stuart L. Pimm, "The Various Christian Ethics of Species Conservation," in *Religion and the New Ecology: Environmental Prudence in a World in Flux* (Notre Dame: University of Notre Dame Press, 2006), 132-133.

95 Ibid.

In each of these, we find a reassuring alignment to environmentalism. And a second scriptural passage, Job 12:7–10 (ESV), encourages us to look to the natural world for answers:

7 "But ask the beasts, and they will teach you;
  the birds of the heavens, and they will tell you;
8 or the bushes of the earth, and they will teach you;
  and the fish of the sea will declare to you.
9 Who among all these does not know
  that the hand of the Lord has done this?
10 In his hand is the life of every living thing
  and the breath of all mankind."

I read this passage as permission to honor the pursuit of science for answers. Is the scientific method not our way of asking the Earth questions?

One of my conservation professors, Dr. Stuart Pimm, co-authored an entire paper about bringing the church's leadership to the forefront of conservation. As a world-renowned scientist and outspoken conservationist, his arguments carry particular weight.

"Maybe it is presumptuous in light of the current political climate to ask ecologists and Christians to find common ground in conservation," he admits. "Yet, that is exactly what we propose."[96] With species already going extinct at a rate one thousand times faster than the background rate, Professor Pimm always told us, common ground between Christians and ecologists is nothing short of urgent.

---

96 Ibid, 118.

The church can play a powerful role in this, but unfortunately, the contemporary church isn't quite there yet. (Pimm actually compares it to Martin Luther King, Jr.'s criticism of the contemporary church's "ineffective" role in civil rights throughout the 1960s, when there were so many opportunities to defend social justice through scripture.)[97]

Many Christians in the United States do not support environmental protection for reasons such as associating environmentalism with evolution, prioritization of the economy, family values, avoidance of Earth-worshipping.

But stewardship, as inscribed in scripture, may call new attention to the environment.

Whether you call it "Creation," "nature," or "biodiversity," that entity is worth saving.

WHEN RELIGION DIVIDES

I remember spending the day at the March for Science several years ago and chatting with an older couple for a few minutes. The March had focused on truth, democracy, science-informed policy, and protecting the climate. Toward the end of our conversation, I recall them saying, "Enjoy the rest of the rally! Make sure to steer clear of the counter-protester over there . . ."

I looked over and saw a young man adorned in cross-shaped buttons and scriptural accessories, holding a sign that read,

---

97   Ibid.

"Love the Lord with all your heart, and all your soul, and all your mind . . ." (Mark 12:30, NIV).

In his other hand, a second flagship Bible verse, John 3:16: "For God so loved the world that he gave his one and only Son, that whoever believes in him shall not perish but have eternal life."

He stared blankly at passersby in his silent, expository protest.

But to me, and probably a few other attendees, his viewpoint didn't necessarily contradict anything we stood for.

"Those verses mean a lot to me, too," I wanted to say to him, "and that's exactly *why* I'm devoted to protecting God's creation at all costs."

However, I was at a loss for words. How could I reassure him some of us didn't view scripture as a "counter-protest" to environmentalism at all? Or that every intricacy of science paradoxically strengthens my faith? Being both a scientist and a Christian, one unfortunately tends to lose credibility on both sides.

But if Christianity somehow included an undying care and respect for the climate, as we see in the stubbornness of nuns, that could be an alliance that saves the climate movement.

One of the most readily available generalizations about climate change denialists is that they are evangelicals. In fact, "Bible thumpers" is one of the "okay, boomer" equivalents referring to more pious, traditional, or fundamentalist Christians in the United States accused of scripture-tethered dogmatism.

There is a moment in the 2006 comedy film *Borat* that aims to capture this exact stereotype, as Kazakhstani pseudo-journalist Borat travels across rural America to discover "America's greatness" through reality TV-style exposition. He attends and films a fundamentalist Christian service in the deep South of the United States, and, when the topic of evolutionary descent from a common ancestor arises, one preacher famously cries, "I didn't evolve out of a monkey! I didn't used to be a tadpole! I is what I is!"[98] That piece of footage in particular was definitely intended to characterize the most extreme, counter-evolutionist perspective end of the belief spectrum.

However, assuming that this is an accurate portrayal of every evangelical Christian in the South is a harmful generalization. Part of the reason why science (whether evolution or climate science) is so ardently *distrusted* in the evangelical movement is because some scientists fail to give religious communities the basic respect and acknowledgement they deserve.

There are extreme Christians, and there are extreme scientists. Agnosticism and skepticism can enshrine the empirical to the point where they belittle anyone whose beliefs extend a little beyond empiricism. On the other end of the spectrum, fundamental Christianity often villainizes scientists

---

98 Nick O, "Borat Goes to Church Part 1," April 16, 2020, video.

as challengers to scriptural truths (to be interpreted literally), including the age of the Earth, the origin of mankind, and the nature of the miracles of Jesus. Nowhere in scripture, however, does an Earth-related verse contradict the pleas of modern activists to stop climate change.

To defeat the image of the elitist, lab coat-wearing scientist, my hope is future generations of scientists be open-minded toward the questions science can't answer. Or have the courage not to claim science can answer everything—even venturing to *admire* faith rather than chuckle at it with scorn or pity.

Likewise, younger Christians will hopefully continue to become more open-minded toward the elements of science that easily coexist with faith beliefs. Perhaps there will be growth in the radical idea that faith can supplement rather than replace science. The firmest fundamentalists might consider viewing science as the framework that upholds the majesty of God's creation.

Overall, the trend among younger generations is to stray from their parents' beliefs and push closer to the moderate middle of the piety spectrum. (Millennials and Gen Zers especially fit this trend. In fact, Gen Z has been called "post-Christian" as its rate of atheism is double that of the general population.[99]) The piety gap between older and younger generations is a strong reason to pursue stewardship, as stewardship can be interpreted religiously or non-religiously. There is ample room for tolerance in stewardship.

---

99   "Atheism Doubles Among Gen Z." Barna Group. January 24, 2018.

By recognizing that neither atheists nor religious folks are completely "blind" to anything, both perspectives avoid slipping further into ideological blindness.

WHEN RELIGION UNIFIES

One year when John Muir was young, he fell into serious illness and awoke one day suffering literal blindness.

It turned out the blindness was temporary, but it took a while for it to go away. When Muir finally regained his sight, the world looked different to him; piercingly colorful, joy-inspiring, and more moving than he could comprehend. From that moment onward, he sought out nature in every moment.

Though Muir was never one to start an organized religion (he was nonetheless known as a "Prophet" of nature), I would venture to call his experience a spiritual awakening. And, I would venture to say it's happened to other Americans, Christian and non-Christian alike, young and old . . .

It happened to Bob Inglis.

I learned that Inglis, featured in earlier chapters of this book, is a Christian.

Inglis always cared about his hometown. However, widespread environmental protection was never really on his radar...until he went on vacation to the Great Barrier Reef.

While on his trip, he met another vacationer who was also a Christian. They became friends and started talking candidly about religion and the world. After spending time with this man and watching him connect spiritually with nature—seeing God and the duty of stewardship in every corner of the Reef—Inglis realized they were kindred spirits. He gained genuine respect for his new acquaintance. Their common values overshadowed any political differences the two may have had.

This experience at the Great Barrier Reef, along with his trip to Antarctica and conversation with his son, led to Inglis's "complete 180" in his environmental views and his courageous advocacy of the Eco-Right movement.

It reminded me of a story from 1903 in which John Muir, President Theodore Roosevelt, and a personal chef wind up disappearing from their camping group to go explore the Yosemite wilderness together for three days. Telling stories, taking in breathtaking views, and shivering through cold nights, Roosevelt and Muir developed an earnest respect for one another.

So positively did they bond on that formative trip, that after their return (much to the relief of the group), President Roosevelt excitedly pushed Congress to pass laws to protect wild lands. He designated wildlife sanctuaries, parks, and national monuments to save millions of acres of public land. Within two years, Roosevelt formed the U.S. Forest Service, leaving behind a conservation legacy that America would cherish for over a century.

* * *

The effect of being awed in Earth's natural spaces (the seeing-the-reef effect) is one of the most powerful ways to get someone of any age to care about climate change. A politician's trip to Antarctica can change his political platform and his life. A three-day romp in the woods with the right naturalist can lead to the establishment of the Forest Service. And sometimes, it doesn't even take other humans to profoundly influence a climate skeptic. Sometimes, nature does the talking.

As a counterargument, flying around the world to visit these places is pretty bad for the climate, right? Admittedly, yes. But while people are rightfully concerned about the high carbon cost of airplane travel without offsets, it is sometimes worth trading that environmental impact for a lifelong worldview impact.

There are two outcomes of such a travel experience: The visitor is 1) awed by beauty of a pristine natural space, and/or 2) sobered by the reality of scenery that has been massively impacted by climate change. And for those generations growing up during the worst of rising ocean temperatures and coral bleaching, it seems the Great Barrier Reef falls perfectly into both categories.

Feeling simultaneously awed and sobered is a description that comes pretty close to having a connection with God.

According to a recent poll, Americans chose "protecting God's creation" as the third most common reason why they want to reduce global warming (12 percent). (The most common reason why Americans want to reduce global warming is to "provide a better life for our children and grandchildren"

(24 percent), followed by "preventing the destruction of most life on the planet" (16 percent)).[100]

It's quite reassuring to see that care for future generations topped the list as the most popular reason—one in four Americans selected that reason—and yet it's also worth pointing out that protecting God's creation, a directly religious objective, made it into the top three.

Could the most religious Americans be untapped allies of the climate movement?

Maybe—there is already a shift in global theology toward the climate.

Pope Francis himself supports a carbon tax.

And when prompted on climate change more generally, he replied,

"The violence that exists in the human heart is also manifest in the symptoms of illness that we see in the earth, the water, the air and in living things."[101]

Suddenly, from one of the most prominent religious figures in the world, we hear pollution and greenhouse gas

---

100 Leiserowitz et al., "Climate Change and the American Mind," 2018.

101 José Santiago, "15 Quotes on Climate Change by World Leaders," World Economic Forum, November 27, 2015.

emissions being equated with violence inside the human heart…violence that stems from the very sin for which we plead forgiveness.

Bulldozers, pipelines, smokestacks, and hazardous waste barrels each take on the role of pathogens—of weapons. They serve as extensions of our own malice, hubris, and violence, all justified by the wrong interpretation of Genesis 1:28's "dominion," and "subdue." Even the book of Revelation, when it warns of apocalypse, foretells of the destruction of the destroyers of the Earth.

As I mentioned earlier, the powerful notion of stewardship doesn't exist in Christianity alone.

The best stewards, and first environmentalists, some would say, have always been Native Americans. Nature, to them, is as alive and sentient as human beings, deserving of unconditional caretaking under the Great Spirit. An animal killed for sustenance is never treated as disposable; all parts are used, validating its sacred and circular existence. And there are many familial embodiments of nature: Brother Eagle, Sister Sky…the idea of Mother Earth herself. Chief Seattle teaches us we do not *inherit* Earth from our ancestors—we borrow it from our children. Spirituality itself was generational. The intertwining of nature, family, and ancestry leads to a universal pantheism and animism firmly founded upon respect for the natural world.

A few other examples include Islam, Judaism, and Hinduism:

In Islam, there is a word for the role of humans as trustees and stewards, *khalifah*. Overexploitation, overconsumption, and overuse of resources thwart the balance the environment and the power of *khalifah* to mitigate the worst of climate change. One line of the Quran reads, "Every living thing is in a state of worship."[102] Professor Odeh Al-Jayyousi comments that whenever one hurts a bird or a plant, that person is silencing a community of worshippers.[103]

In Judaism, a great example comes from the Old Testament's story of Noah, who faithfully saved species from the Great Flood in pairs of two. Rabbi David Saperstein declares, "So now we must ask ourselves: Will we, at this moment when so many species are vulnerable, be partners in God's covenant with creation?"[104]

In Hinduism, it is believed that harming another living being (whether an animal, plant, or human) means harming God's cosmic body of which one is a part. Man is taught to live in harmony with the world, rather than viewing Earth as hostile or attempting a conquest of it.[105]

---

102 Odeh Al-Jayyousi, "How Islam Can Represent a Model for Environmental Stewardship," UN Environment Programme, June 21, 2018.

103 Ibid.

104 Van Houtan and Pimm, "Christian Ethics," 126.

105 Harold Coward, "Hindu Views of Nature and the Environment," 2003, in Helaine Selin (eds), *Nature Across Cultures: Views of Nature and the Environment in Non-Western Cultures*, vol. 4, 411.

Countless other religions and belief systems hold similar truths (consider Taoism's emphasis on the mysticism of nature, or Buddhism's mantra of "do no harm").

And, of course, even atheism and agnosticism leave room for a rather scientific "intelligence with the earth" between Nature and the Individual that simply recognizes the organic nature of human bodies. *Shall I not have intelligence with the earth? Am I not partly leaves and vegetable mould myself?*

Starting as early as the Romantic literary period in the 1800s, authors, poets, and artists explored the phenomenon of the "sublime," unifying the terrifying and beautiful force of Nature with the Individual.

John Muir explored that union almost a century later in one of my favorite stories of his: becoming part of a windstorm.

Muir wanted to experience the tempest from a tree's perspective, so he fastened himself to a hundred-foot-tall Douglas spruce in the mountains of California. The storm raged around him; the smell of needles and resin filled the air. He closed his eyes, leaned against the tree trunk on the bare cliff-slope, and listened.

The storm died down.

Muir waited for the wind to stop, unfastened himself, and climbed down "with a consummate sense of peace."[106]

---

106 Jedediah Purdy, *After Nature: A Politics for the Anthropocene* (Cambridge: Harvard University Press, 2015), 116.

Where he expected to find violence, he found harmony. He had found the sublime.

Poet and naturalist Wendell Berry summarizes this chapter most appropriately.

"...*We must learn to acknowledge that the creation is full of mystery; we will never clearly understand it. We must abandon arrogance and stand in awe. We must recover the sense of the majesty of the creation, and the ability to be worshipful in its presence. For it is only on the condition of humility and reverence before the world that our species will be able to remain in it.*"[107]

It is up to you whether to approach that reverence through the lens of Scripture or the individualistic awe of John Muir. The important part is that we *unify* in our benevolent "dominion" over the Earth.

In that union we will understand the simplest truth of saving stewardship: We can only continue to glorify God on a living planet.

...A truth that nuns have known all along.

---

107 Wendell Berry, *Recollected Essays, 1965–1980*, in Nash, *American Environmentalism*, 278.

CHAPTER 8

PROTECT YOUR PATCH

———

The foot of man becomes thus fastened to the earth. He constructs his dwelling place to outlast his own existence. It passes as a heritage to his children [...] the mountain that borders the horizon, immoveable and unchanging in the lapse of years, and insensibly leading the mind from the transient objects of time to the boundless ages of eternity, all silent witnesses of the first emotions of infancy and the dearest joys of youth, grappled to the soul by ever multiplying recollections, **chain the heart of man to his home,** *and become the primary elements in that strong, beneficent and virtuous impulse,* **the love of his country.**

—JOHN QUINCY ADAMS

Think of your hometown for a minute.

Wherever you remember growing up—hold that place in your mind.

For most of us, it's easy. There's a warm feeling of familiarity and comfort. There's a certain smell that is impossible to pinpoint. There's that one safe place that comes to mind, perhaps a refuge in a grove of trees, on a rooftop, along a riverbank, or in some special and undiscovered corner of the town.

My hometown isn't much of a town to begin with. I was raised in the rural countryside of Maryland, at the base of Sugarloaf Mountain. Between long stretches of hidden houses tucked away in rustic woodlands, sometimes the only sign of development is the singular road that winds steadily toward the mountain, pavement conceding to gravel and then to grass.

I ran, hiked, and explored the twists and turns of that road for eighteen years. I soon developed a fascination with the mountain landscape, collecting "geological samples" from each cliffside for my egg-carton rock collection, as well as an eye for the scientific beauty of its ecosystems I observed in every hawk migration or sparring of bucks. In the summer, my family and I would often pick blackberries in the mornings, swim in the creek in hot afternoons, and stroll down the road in the evenings to witness spectacular sunsets.

From my bedroom window, I could see the orange sky, latticed with airplane trails, illuminating acres of rolling farmland home to horses and cows who greeted me on every distance run. The foreground was always cows, and the background was always Sugarloaf Mountain. For that matter, Sugarloaf Mountain isn't much of a mountain to begin with. It's more of a lopsided hill that leans idiosyncratically to one side, as if Mother Earth had sensed my fascination, taken her palm to the rocky slope, and nudged it an inch closer to my house. With no towns or developments nearby, I grew up enjoying the company of my parents and twin brother rather than traditional neighbors, romping through the mountain's trails rather than watching cable, and falling asleep to the wail of coyotes rather than police sirens.

The peaceful isolation that once frustrated me endlessly as a child is something I now view as one of the greatest blessings in my life.

Though many environmentally conscious individuals differ in their values and approaches to protecting the Earth, if there's one thing I've found we all have in common, it's this type of backstory: a formative childhood experience with the natural world. Young Rachel Carson grew up in a small river town with her mother, who also appreciated nature and biology. As a child, Jane Goodall once spent five hours lurking in a henhouse just to watch how a hen lays an egg. (At two years old, Jane received a stuffed toy chimpanzee from her mother, which she still has today.)

And maybe you have too. Regardless of people's age, environmental views, or political identity, the sense of protection we feel toward our hometowns is a nearly universal quality. Nature, especially, provides the safe space our human nature seeks out. (As much as I hesitate to say "safe space" for fear of fulfilling the stereotype of sensitive Gen Z snowflakes, the reality is that everyone is entitled to that Safe Space in nature.) There are few corners of a city to escape the nine-to-five corporate bustle, and, in an era of digital lifestyles within the home, even fewer places to find complete privacy and solitude.

* * *

In light of this, I wanted to speak with someone local. Who protects the land I consider home? I found someone who is largely responsible for maintaining the agricultural reserve that stretches across regions like my hometown in Maryland: Dolores Milmoe. Dolores is an esteemed protector of the Montgomery County Agricultural Reserve and a force to be reckoned with in local politics.

Dolores tells me she grew up playing outside in the woods every day and was taught by Catholic nuns who regularly took nature field trips. At home and in a nearby forest, she would spend her time swinging from vines, building little tree huts, and exploring many aspects of the natural world.

Her biggest piece of advice on mobilizing people of all ages and all backgrounds on environmental protection consists of three simple words: Protect your patch. Think about it—a hometown, a city, a rural region, or simply a *place of origin*, is something held in common by every single American. And the emotional ties people have to their hometowns resonate as lucidly in old age as they do during childhood. "I remember clearly, even now, being eight years old and taking a field trip…and all the kids are going into this forest…and there is this beautiful, clear, running brook making all these wonderful sounds…and light is coming through the trees," Dolores chuckles, sounding wistful. "It had a huge impact on me."

After moving out, Dolores later returned to her childhood home as a slightly older kid, only to find that both the house and the forest around it had been completely torn down.

"I was twelve years old, and it made me so sad and angry," she told me. She explained how her early experiences witnessing the wonder of nature, and then seeing it ruined by development, propelled her to fight back against landscape destruction.

Though she pursued her academic background in art, switching back and forth between art and science seemed like second nature to her. She is now fully an advocate. "Well, now, instead of painting landscapes, I'm trying to save them."

Dolores works creatively to protect the agricultural and forested reserves in my home state of Maryland. She began by successfully protecting an old, beautiful forested lot in Takoma Park, Maryland by launching a door-to-door grassroots initiative to gain support. If a picture is worth a thousand words, a well-made GIS map is worth a million. (GIS, or geographical information system, is a computerized technology that helps environmentalists visualize landscapes from above using satellite imagery. It's a really powerful tool for showing landscape change—people care the most about what they can see!)

Speaking cross-generationally, older advocates like Dolores are excited for younger generations to train in technological solutions like GIS and data visualization programs. Utilizing her fine art skills, she has also created logos, maps, videos, and promotional materials publicizing the importance of the land we take for granted and all of its ecosystem services and its role in shaping Maryland culture.

Her work is not always easy or easily accepted. In 1995, the Saudi Arabian government wanted to build an expansive academy for 3,500 students, obliterating over 500 acres of prime farmland in the county's nationally acclaimed Agricultural Reserve, south of the town of Poolesville. The land happened to be over a federally designated Sole Source Aquifer holding precious groundwater, the only source of potable water for the town and surrounding farm community. (Dolores and her nonprofit group had earlier instituted the process to have the aquifer designated and protected with a formal petition to the EPA.) In the Saudi Academy fight, she described the endless hearings and behind-the-scenes work that went into organizing to protect the farmland, as well as the challenges that came from testifying in front of the local Poolesville government with an all-female team of advocates. "I thought we had just stepped back into 1950." She remembers being called an "outsider," at best, and at worst, one of "the infidel housewives."

Yet, when you are an environmental advocate fighting the battle to protect your patch, the name calling fades into the background and the legwork becomes second nature. Before the developers could begin annexing the land, Dolores and her team worked hard to bring in scientists (hydrologists) and consult with them. They tried even harder to petition for a referendum in Poolesville, gathering thousands of signatures…and won the vote opposing the annexation to build the academy. After the referendum, the Saudis sold the property and Dolores's group worked with the new landowner to place the land in a permanent conservation easement. Those 525 acres will be protected forever.

* * *

In addition to this victory, Dolores has taken on other dilemmas of land management: *Should we really build industrial-sized solar panel installations here if it means it will decimate this part of the reserve, its forests, its ecosystem, and food production potential? How do we deal with rural homeowners using chainsaws to covertly widen designated rustic roads, incentivizing speeding and making them less safe?*

In the wake of her advocacy successes, she has been threatened and called a "redheaded bitch," which she says she wears as a badge of honor. Often, it's mainly older, wealthier people in power who fight over land use. With young people, local policy offers plenty of opportunities for generational bridging, working with volunteers, students, and interns. However, there is a shortage of young people in local government leadership positions in Montgomery County. Mentorship, the primary channel to leadership, is where we agreed there is the most hope and opportunity to inspire future local leaders.

Through leaders and mentors like Dolores, I've learned never to underestimate the power of local politics.

I've learned what it means to "protect your patch."

CHAPTER 9

THE POWER OF MUSIC AND MEDIA

—

There needs to be a massive outcry—a choir of voices—by the American people demanding change.

—LOIS GIBBS

BEFORE THE DELUGE

The lyrics to Jackson Browne's "Before the Deluge" read like poetry.[108]

Browne released the song in 1974, and it will always be regarded as one of the most profound compositions about the destruction of Earth and an entire generation's "fall from grace."

---

108 *Stage Parades*, "Jackson Browne—Before the Deluge (+ lyrics 1974),"
August 3, 2012, video.

So powerful and simplistic are the melodies of this song that I would advise pausing your reading to go search it up on YouTube and listen as you read. In fact, the comments section is a rare goldmine of unity and civility as viewers praise Browne's songwriting and reflect together on what the lyrics mean. One comment reads, "I once thought the song was about my generation. At seventy, I realize it's true of all generations."[109]

This song has been described as "pre-apocalyptic." Browne wrote it during a time of environmental turmoil; through the 1970s, the United States faced widespread pollution, the oil crisis, poor air quality, unregulated hazardous waste, and uncertainties about whether nascent environmental legislation would be enough to counteract this destruction. These lyrics can also be heard through the lens of a nuclear apocalypse, as many Americans feared and protested the possibility of nuclear war.

Though fears of imminent nuclear war in the United States have calmed somewhat in today's society, fears of climate change perfectly echo those expressed in "Before the Deluge." The deluge itself is a Biblical allusion to the great flood of Genesis, symbolic of whatever irreversible climate damage awaits us before we've heeded the warnings of creation. Today, IPCC reports and tipping-point research studies give us a concrete look at what this deluge, if not prevented, would entail.

---

109 Ibid, comments section.

What's most interesting about these lyrics is how they describe the transition from passion to complacency among Browne's generation. He talks about how youth, once flying around with a crazed passion for activism, trade in the fragile glow of their youthful determination for the resignation of living a lavish, glittery, and comfortable adult life.

Are we, as millennials and Gen Zers, not accused of the same shortcomings?

Purchasing twenty-four-pack bottles of diet soda from the very companies whose single-use philosophies we condemn?

Reconciling our disdain for carbon emissions with our obligatory dream of traveling the world?

Buying a sleek new apartment sitting on a lot that was a forest months earlier?

Using social media to document ourselves—our athleticism, our socialite statuses, our makeup prowess—rather than our values?

Avoiding conversations about climate change for being inherently "unsexy?"

Because twenty-first century consumer society, too, is structured around both hedonism and convenience, it's hard to hear Jackson Browne's lyrics and not think of the world today. From a cynical perspective, this resigned materialism is a failure that adolescent boomers, millennials, and Gen Zers tend to have in common. Thus, some have speculated we've again reached a dead end in the long-term mobilization of social movements; comfort dominates action because activism is inherently *un*comfortable. Laziness is part of human nature and is therefore something we must transcend together.

However, acknowledging our common shortcomings between the 1970s and now, expressed through a medium as universal as music, is the first step to taking very tangible action. In fact, music itself may be the force that can topple twenty-first century consumerism if today's entertainment industry can revive or echo the mainstream environmental messages that permeated so strongly in the 1960s–1980s. We'll delve into the power of music as the conscience of society, and whether it's attainable for today's artists to boldly address climate change in the same style of Jackson Browne, Bob Dylan, Joni Mitchell, Crosby Stills & Nash, Marvin Gaye, Cat Stevens, Pete Seeger, Three Dog Night, and the canon of protest folk/rock/soul music that lay the groundwork for the birth of a nationwide, bipartisan environmental conscience.

MAINSTREAM MATTERS

Part of what made those decades so special was the emergence of the artist-activist: celebrity musicians who considered activism so central to their identity that they were often encountered on the streets, or politically engaged in Washington, alongside everyone else.

My dad had two such encounters with artist-activists he remembers distinctly.

During his gap year at UC Santa Barbara, he found himself at a Sierra Club demonstration at the Diablo Canyon nuclear power plant in San Luis Obispo, California. The site was dangerously vulnerable to tsunamis, earthquakes, and disasters that had been warned of at Japan's Fukushima reactor, so a large crowd gathered there to protest the environmental risks it posed.

"I saw somebody sitting there on a wall, playing the guitar and singing," my dad recalls, "and it was Jackson Browne." The musician sat maybe ten feet away from him, just playing songs about the environment. My dad and his friends listened raptly. The coolest part, in his words, was seeing such a famous artist just hanging out and "being an activist like the rest of us were."

Another time, at the White House's signing ceremony of the Alaska Lands Act, my dad remembers seeing some big names in attendance, including President Jimmy Carter himself—for obvious reasons—as well as the Rockefellers, who had become eco-philanthropists themselves. He remembers spotting one celebrity in particular: John Denver. (You might be familiar with his hit "Take Me Home, Country Roads," a pro-conservation anthem whose lyrics have now become recognizable far beyond the mountains of West Virginia they celebrate.) My dad almost bumped into him walking along to another room in the White House.

"Hey John, you know, I want to shake your hand and thank you for helping to advocate for the passage of the Alaska Lands Act." My dad smiled. "And for choosing to use your celebrity status and clout to do so."

John Denver returned a warm smile. "Well, of course. What's your name?"

"Dave Reeves."

"And where do you work, Dave?"

"I work for the Alaska Coalition."

The musician chuckled. "Why, I should be the one thanking *you* and shaking *your* hand for all that you did to make this possible!"

His gratitude was sincere. It was an era in which music activism was mainstream enough for John Denver himself to show up at the White House.

Forty years later, I think my father is still a little starstruck.

* * *

Jackson Browne and John Denver are just two examples of artist-activists interacting humbly with the world as real people who have decided to make activism, as well as art, part of their identity.

When the public gets to know and respect a celebrity *first* as an artist, and then as an environmentalist, it makes everyone more receptive to the environmental messages that are woven into their songs over time.

(If Justin Bieber or Ariana Grande were to release even a mediocre song about climate change right now and show up at a rally—like Jackson Browne—to sing it alongside the anxious youngsters comprising their fanbase, their actions could help elevate climate policies to the level of national attention they deserve.)

And even if it's not mainstream to release an entire CD of environment-related songs, releasing a single song has proven to be effective, such as Michael Jackson's international chart-topper "Earth Song." It was the last song Michael Jackson sang before his death in 2009, and it is still regarded as one of history's greatest environmental anthems, coming from one of history's greatest artists.

Big-name artists matter in the twenty-first century. They are like the influencers we discussed in Chapter 4—omnipresent, idolized, and great social media discussion-starters. However, big-name artists have a long way to go from the perspective of modern *ecomusicology*.

Ecomusicology is a rather cool word for studying the role of nature or environmentalism in music.[110] By examining music across multiple genres through an ecomusicology lens, we start to see how nature emerges in much subtler ways in modern song lyrics and how their genres have evolved beyond the folk-rock canon built by previous generations.

---

110 "What is Ecomusicology?" *Ecomusicology Review.*

We also start to see which artists are courageous enough to offer insights into the world's injustices when it's so much easier to merely offer listeners an escape from them.

WHERE HAVE ALL THE EARTH SONGS GONE?

Think of a song about climate change or the environment released in the past five years that resonates in society. The past ten years? There aren't many that come to mind, and the Top 40 list is particularly devoid. Fifty years ago, protest songs and environmental songs regularly "trended" (if you will, in a pre-internet context) in popular culture, coinciding with "trending" legislation. In the wake of whale overhunting and the Marine Mammals Protection Act of 1972, for example, Crosby, Stills, & Nash released the moving, mourning "To the Last Whale" and projected footage of the creatures swimming as a backdrop to their live concerts.

But if a song is published with an environmental message today, it is regarded as a courageous exception to the status quo.

Now, what I want to do is avoid reading off of the script of "today's music is so shallow, materialistic, and explicitly objectifying of women. It promotes expensive cars and narcissism rather than the issues that matter." The mental image most often paired with this complaint consists of a disillusioned parent or grandparent shaking their fist at whatever their kid elects to blast through the speaker. A complaint like this one is problematic to some extent—it diminishes the thousands of world-changing songs that do integrate the sincerity of civil protest and the compassion of advocacy into their overarching musical messages, including indie artists. With the abundance of music available online in massive streaming libraries, there are too many exceptions to this complaint for it to apply to *all* music. But what about the most popular music?

Comparing the most "popular" music today to that of fifty years ago reveals a huge shift in both genres and cultural values. A shift away from...the quintessential protest song? I hesitate to even try to define what a quintessential protest song would sound like—it can span multiple genres and take any form.

Today, a lot of pop protest songs center around female empowerment and speaking hard truths about sexual harassment in light of the #MeToo Movement (songs like "'Til It Happens to You" by Lady Gaga (2015) or "Un Violador en Tu Camino," the Chilean chant that kicked off #MeToo globally in 2019). Similarly, a lot of rap, hip-hop, and soul/R&B songs serve as protest statements aiming to undermine the racial inequities in the United States and promote racial justice alongside the #BlackLivesMatter Movement (Childish Gambino's "This is America" (2018) and Andra Day's "Rise Up" (2015) are two fantastic examples).

So, while the vast majority of today's popular music tends to center thematically on personal wealth, status, sexual allure, and romantic drama, there are also plenty of modern protest songs—quite meaningful ones—that have successfully emerged into the popular sphere.

The question we should be asking is not why is today's music so shallow, but instead, when will the #FridaysForFuture New Environmental Movement get its own genre of popular music?

There is one music video in particular, called "Earth" by Lil Dicky (2019), that brings me immense hope.

He sings directly about climate change through animated animals (voiced by dozens of celebrities, such as John Legend, Miley Cyrus, Wiz Khalifa, and a very enthusiastic Leonardo DiCaprio).[111] These mainstream artists all came together in a pop single that is somehow both wholesome and explicit, speaking humorously and candidly to my generation about "getting our shit together." I would also recommend taking time to watch "Earth," and notice how the character of the lyrics addresses a completely different generation from the traditional protest song. ("Are we gonna die?" sings Justin Bieber, as a baboon. "You know what, Bieber? We might die.")

But the cynical song ends with a truly powerful chorus and a call to action about how we can work together to save the planet. And maybe this irreverent song is the perfect combination of cynically youthful and funny lyrics, cute animals, and the ethos of big-name artists to shape into something new: the modern environmental protest song.

We can remain hopeful that more artists step up to the plate to popularize messages on climate change, cover old protest

111 *Lil Dicky,* "Lil Dicky——Earth (Official Music Video)," April 19, 2019, video.

songs in tribute, or put out ecomusicological messages as simple as "We Love the Earth."

THE RAGING GRANNIES

Perhaps my favorite intergenerational climate activism encounter of all time was when I was introduced to a music group by the name of "The Raging Grannies."

I was at the fall 2019 Raleigh Climate Strike when I first heard the Grannies take the stage. It was a warm mid-afternoon day in September (I would have been in biology class), and although the climate strike had drawn in great energy and participation from the crowd, it had reached a point when the Friday afternoon lull settled in between speakers. People shielded their eyes from the sun and craned their necks toward the makeshift stage set up in front of Raleigh's Halifax Mall.

A strike organizer leaned over the podium. "Next, I'd like to introduce some of our favorite climate activists, the Raging Grannies!"

A troupe of half a dozen grannies shuffled to the center of the stage and leaned over their microphones. Though their intentionally frumpy hats, bonnets, and aprons signaled some sort of performance, I had no idea they were going to break out in song.

With no background music needed, the ladies launched into an a cappella rendition of what sounded like an old climate protest song, put to the music of a familiar tune.

At first, the audience chuckled wryly and snapped pictures of the Grannies. I'm sure they made it onto a few Snapchat stories—their opening act seemed too adorably outdated not to film.

However, within just a few minutes, the audiences started singing along. Their music had more variation and catchy stamina than the chants we were used to. The Grannies had put the snarky lyrics of each song to a recognizable (sometimes modern) melody, allowing everyone to join in. I felt like we had stepped back in time—or they had stepped forward in time to join us. It was a pleasant and grounding experience.

The student-organized event of over 1,500 people was deemed an overall success. But the Raging Grannies were the stars of the strike!

I hummed to myself on the carpool ride back to campus.

* * *

I reached out to Vicki Ryder, one of the Grannies in the Triangle (Raleigh-Durham-Chapel Hill) chapter. I later learned they refer to their singing groups as "gaggles."

Vicki and I met in my favorite cafe in Durham for breakfast.

She had short gray hair and wore a scarf covered in peace signs. "I really did grow up in the grassroots," explained Vicki, who is a second-generation activist. "I've been in the struggle since 1942."

Yet she exuded a fierce spark of youthful energy, the kind that makes you think, *I would want her on my team.*

Vicki always felt as though activism ran deep in her blood.

"I was named 'Vicki' after 'victory' itself," she said to me, two bites into our breakfast. Her parents had chosen the name out of hope for a quick victory over then-growing fascism. She has since lived out her name in a similar vein of justice and determination, using activism to thwart oppression.

I asked her which issues she was most passionate about, and she told me she's been involved in addressing both environmental and non-environmental causes over the years, including climate change, sexism, racism, corporate greed, and intolerance. The Grannies scope out events to attend relating to all those issues. "We cover pretty much all of the 'isms,'" Vicki remarked.

I had more questions about the Grannies themselves. How does one become a Granny? Who are they?

The Grannies started off as an irreverent nonviolent protest group in Victoria, British Colombia, in 1987. They fought on a local level, particularly on nuclear issues. Some of their first actions included sending "Un-Valentines" to the chairman of the defense committee to express their broken hearts at his negligence on addressing nuclear policy (on Valentine's Day), singing a satirical lullaby under an umbrella full of holes to represent the irrationality of sheltering under a nuclear umbrella, and showing up to a legislative hearing on uranium mining with a laundry basket full of women's underwear, symbolizing the "briefs" they wished to present at the hearings…and poking fun at the "stuffy, often pompous process of such hearings."[112]

I'm sure #FridaysForFuture and Extinction Rebellion activists borrow some of their street-theater creativity from the same handbook.

Before long, people were charmed by the Raging Grannies, both by their wit and by the maternal shamelessness with which they dissented on local issues. The Grannies spread into the United States and formed gaggles around the globe.

They fact-check. They crash parties. They show up to hearings and events (sometimes invited).

Above all, the central goal of their philosophy is to take part in what is known as "grannying." Grannying includes, but is not limited to:

- **Dressing up** in innocent grandmotherly clothes (it helps you approach the target).
- **Writing songs**, to the tune of people's favorites, that "skewer modern wrongs."
- **Satirizing evildoing** in public and getting everyone singing about it.
- **Carrying on the historical legacy** of women in activism who knew what they stood for.

---

112 Carole Roy, "The Original Raging Grannies: Using Creative and Humorous Protests for Political Education," The Raging Grannies Herstory.

- **Exposing corruption** that has been hidden to protect profits. Examples include nuclear waste products being quietly dumped outside of a small town, asbestos sites employing young folks who are desperate for work, and laws being passed so hastily as to sidestep vital community input. Talk about protecting future generations through grassroots activism.

One statement on their website reads, "Grannying is the least understood yet most powerful weapon we have."[113]

I asked Vicki more about her personal experience grannying.

Vicki first found the Grannies after searching for a local community of like-minded activists. She has grannied for several years and in multiple locations in the United States. After moving to Durham with her husband, she joined the local gaggle of Grannies. She disclosed that she writes a lot of their songs herself.

"That's fantastic!" I exclaimed to her, having enjoyed poring over so many witty titles the night before on their website. She then explained her background in music. Growing up, she would attend folk festivals and picket line marches with her parents; she was truly raised on the protest songs of the union labor movement and the civil rights struggles of the 50s and 60s.

"Oh, and Pete Seeger was the music teacher at the school where I was teaching second grade," Vicki remarked rather casually.

---

113 Our Philosophy," The Raging Grannies.

"*The* Pete Seeger?" I stammered.

"Yep."

We both laughed.

Vicki's love for folk music, and especially for protest songs as a catalyst for social change, has been with her literally her entire life.

In addition to being surrounded by parents and fellow teachers who inspired her, Vicki has always been a strong writer. There is a role for everyone in the Raging Grannies, she explained, and she found hers in songwriting.

Crafting song lyrics came with its own frustrations—the Grannies would sometimes run into trouble when they would be asked to perform somewhere only to have to hand over song sheets to be "screened" in advance by event organizers. Rebels at heart and believers in free speech, the gaggle found this infuriating. Vicki reassured me the Grannies are *always* nonviolent protesters who are open to singing in front of receptive and less receptive audiences. But they would refuse to sing in a place where they would be censored on the basis of being "controversial."

Finally, I asked her about the challenges of intergenerational climate activism specifically. She had mentioned the Grannies sing about all the 'isms, but how do they feel about the *ageism* (age-based prejudices) that certainly must underpin their reputation?

I was surprised to hear that ageism seems to be what empowers the Grannies. Consider their stereotypically frumpy costumes. "That's the point," Vicki grinned. People underestimate the Grannies based on their stereotypes about grandmothers being weak or passive. It makes their rebellion all the more beautiful and noteworthy.

At the same time, I've noticed how proudly activists who are Vicki's age embrace the roles of maternal or paternal caretakers for future generations. They *know* about economic inequality and the powers that (still) be. They approach environmental crises with the protective ferocity of a concerned parent. And, like the true stereotype of an aging parent, reputation and embarrassment don't matter to them. Our democracy does. They are relentless activists who have also grown up in the grassroots.

The Raging Grannies are not alone. Similar older-activist groups exist, one of which is Elders Climate Action. While Elder's Climate Action focuses more on bipartisan pro-climate voting and less on civil disobedience, both organizations are fairly similar in their age demographic and their mission to make positive change in the world for future generations.

...And there's lot they can teach us.

So, whenever Greta Thunberg declares "you have failed us" to entire generations of policymakers sitting in front of her, my mind wanders back to the Raging Grannies.

Not these guys, I think to myself. *They've tried pretty damn hard.*

And the fight's not even over.

CHAPTER 10

CLIMATE GRIEF, ECO-ANXIETY, AND OTHER SENTIMENTS THAT MAKE US "SNOWFLAKES"

There is a sacredness in tears. They are not the mark of weakness, but of power. They speak more eloquently than ten thousand tongues. They are the messengers of overwhelming grief, of deep contrition, and of unspeakable love.

—WASHINGTON IRVING

"Do the students roll out nap mats and curl up in the fetal position with their blankies and pacifiers while listening to her lectures?"

This was just one reaction to Dr. Jennifer Atkinson's new class on climate grief: dealing with the anxiety and psychological effects that arise as we come face to face with climate change.

Her students' reactions? Filling every single seat in the class during registration.

Clearly, the concept of a class taught on climate grief is too much for some to handle. Words like "Climate grief," "Eco-anxiety," and all permutations of environment + loss + stress certainly didn't exist twenty years ago, but they arguably define my generation. We are existential thinkers. In fact, Dictionary.com selected "existential" as the Word of the Year for 2019.[114] (Searches surged up 179 percent after candidate Bernie Sanders called climate change "an existential crisis that impacts not just you and me and our generation but our kids and our grandchildren.") Dictionary.com cited climate change awareness as a primary driver of the "existential zeitgeist" we saw wrapping up the 2010s, also mentioning Hong Kong protests, Brexit, Big Tech, Notre Dame's fire, wildlands on fire, gun violence, and the outbreak of coronavirus as issues that challenge us to look metaphysically at the human experience.

How do we come to terms with loss? That question persists in an era of existentialism. Even our collective sense of humor is growing existential, as it banks on a darkly introspective meme culture. The cynicism of our meme culture is contrasted rather sharply by what we see in Dr. Atkinson's classroom: vulnerability, fear, and confronting loss. And a willingness—enthusiasm, even—to talk about it together.

---

114 "Dictionary.com's Word of the Year for 2019 Is…," Dictionary.com.

FACING CLIMATE GRIEF

Dr. Atkinson, a professor at the University of Washington–Bothell, originally created the Climate Grief class because she noticed the toll climate change was taking on her Gen Z students. Some soon-to-be environmental majors were abandoning the idea altogether because the field was just "too depressing." Soon after the local media started reporting on Dr. Atkinson's class, the initial praise she received for her innovation was joined by criticism and mockery like what we saw above. In her words, "a flood of derisive emails and phone calls poured into my office, and the newspaper comment sections filled up with responses mocking today's 'absurd' college courses and the students who attend them."

The only thing that struck me more than hearing about the class itself was this reaction to it.

It sounded like the classic spawn of the YouTube comments section, where no one is safe from mockery or scrutiny, as students in the class were mocked as "coddled" or "wimpy" and were simply told they need to grow up.[115] This form of parental scolding is a common theme in intergenerational feuding and points to a far deeper wound between generations. Some climate skeptics from older generations feel as though their hardened upbringing—whether it be the Great Depression, war drafts, or the economic stagnancy of an energy crisis— justifies their derision toward the seemingly hypersensitive young people who are more inclined to share their fears and political complaints openly on social media.

---

115 Jennifer Atkinson, "My Students Aren't Snowflakes, They're Badasses," *The Denver Post*, June 1, 2018.

So, Gen Zers become the scapegoat for the realization that American values have shifted from conformity and consistency to intersectionality and identity validation.

On the other side, Gen Zers often fail to recognize the fact that older generations have faced their own challenges on an existential scale. Events like the Cuban Missile Crisis, and the larger uncertainty toward a nuclear crisis during the Cold War, reverberated on the same scale as climate change in terms of the level of potential damage, but they were handled as threats with far more urgency and immediacy. Members of older generations all know what it is like to grow up feeling scared as a teenager for one reason or another, and that's a starting point from which we can build empathy as climate activists. Regardless, in the same way it would have seemed insensitive to mock a "Nuclear Fallout Anxiety" class during the Cold War, it is a harmful choice to use scornful language like "pacifiers" and "fetal position" to mock kids who are freaked out about climate change.

I reached out to Dr. Atkinson to hear her side of things. She reacted to criticism with a simple statement: Climate grief isn't snowflake—it's badass. She explained to me that denial is a *default*, not just for climate change, but for any pressing generational crisis. In the face of so much despair toward rampant wildfires, melting Arctic Ice, extreme weather, and loss of biodiversity across the planet, Dr. Atkinson and her students have the courage to be afraid, daring to openly discuss the psychological toll of what could be a slowly unfolding apocalypse.

Dr. Atkinson's journey in teaching climate grief began when she sensed the distress of her students. One student from Puerto Rico, for instance, developed chronic anxiety after Hurricane Maria, struggling to concentrate in school as he thought about whether his family would recover their homes, jobs, and ability to even visit the region.

"For years, I had noticed students were walking around with dark clouds over their head, feeling depressed over political inaction, grief toward wildlife extinction, and anxiety about their future...but also the sense of anger and betrayal at the inaction of older generations. And there just wasn't a space to talk about that," Dr. Atkinson explained.

Gen Z and millennial students are still grappling with these massive existential questions: *What does it mean to come of age at a moment when our entire life support systems are being destabilized? What does it mean to inherit a dying world? If I have children, what kind of nightmare could they grow up in?*

In 2017, the American Psychological Association released a report on the mental health consequences of extreme weather—including trauma—along with the confirmation that "gradual, long-term changes in climate can also surface a number of different emotions, including fear, anger, feelings of powerlessness, or exhaustion."[116] Part of the message of Dr. Atkinson's class is that we need to lean into these emotions. "[We] really do need to process this information on an

---

116 Susan Clayton et al., Mental Health and Our Changing Climate: Impacts, Implications, and Guidance," Washington, D.C.: American Psychological Association and ecoAmerica, 2017.

emotional level, if we're going to fully digest it on cognitive level," she asserts.

Because she teaches in Washington state, she told me that she and her students have always been in close proximity to wildfires and poor air quality—on their campus, climate change was tangible. (Students along the east coast, meanwhile, suffer the damage and uncertainty of extreme hurricanes and storm surges. The U.S. will soon be characterized by the regionally defined damage of climate change.) "Climate grief" itself is defined as any form of fear, anxiety, depression, or mourning over climate change, particularly coming from young people.

The problem is that we don't openly talk about these climate-driven emotions in our society, nor are the philosophical questions underpinning climate anxiety central to physical sciences curriculum. Is climate anxiety something to address in educational curricula as early as elementary or middle school? It would be hard to do so when discussing the climate, in any context, is so difficult in many states' public schools. Part of the generational divide here comes from whether or not these questions should be factored into physical sciences curriculum, accompany it in any way, or at least be discussed in an informal parent-to-child context. Understanding climate change has become a basic literacy needed to understand the twenty-first century.[117] Climate anxiety support groups exist on Facebook, consisting mainly

---

117 Paola Rosa-Aquino, "The Life-Altering, World-Ending Topic They're Still Not Teaching You About in School, *Grist*, June 4, 2019.

of young adults, function for the same reasons: to provide solidarity and climate literacy.

BLISSONANCE AND SOLASTALGIA

What and what?

These are the two new words Dr. Atkinson offered me to add to my twenty-first century vocabulary.

The first one, blissonance, describes the feeling you get when walking outside to gorgeous seventy-five degree weather only to realize, in a flash of dissonance, that it is not supposed to be this warm in the middle of January. You enjoy the sunshine secretly but find it hard to savor a day that is tainted by eerie abnormality.

The second word, solastalgia, has a bit of a nuanced definition. When your hometown, or any familiar landscape, becomes so drastically altered by the climate (flooded, eroded, burned) that it is unrecognizable, you experience the gloomy emotion of solastalgia, meaning nostalgia or homesickness for a place you've never left.

I find myself dealing with solastalgia all the time. I feel it snorkeling, skiing, and hiking in the Everglades. The experience always feels bittersweet, or tainted, at the thought of the place being taken from me.

The reason why it's important to talk about climate grief and to use the odd language of these recently coined words is so that climate activists of any age or background have our own language to share in the coming century as we confront new experiences for which we don't yet have the words.

"Since environmentalists and front-line communities are confronting this crisis head on, their anger and anxiety only gets magnified when so few people around them are even talking about this existential threat," Dr. Atkinson remarked in a local news article. "Our class is an antidote to that collective denial and invalidation."[118]

How do you experience climate grief?

Have you, or will you, worry for friends and relatives during natural disasters?

Are you someone who mourns the silencing of nature?

Fewer songbirds sing in our backyards, rivers empty of fish, the sounds of frogs at night are disappearing. The world industrializes and develops.

I tend to grieve at the inevitability of that development, as the starry skies that usually provide me comfort and answers fade behind lamplight.

It feels like I'm in a car headed straight for the path of an innocent animal; even if I try my hardest to swerve and the car ends up hitting the creature, I will feel personally

118 Blake Peterson, "UW Bothell Seminar Aims to Help Students Cope with Climate Change Concerns," *Bothell-Kenmore Reporter*, February 21, 2018.

responsible for owning the vehicle that brought about its premature death.

My own planetary citizenship is something I want to enjoy and cherish, but it always has that backdrop of guilty anxiety.

It is valuable for you to self-reflect on your own anxieties.

If you feel like a sense of helplessness clouds your path, know that's okay. The environmentalist's fatigue is heavy. Being a witness to deterioration—in any form—is wearing on the spirit.

But a mixture of grief and fear, in some form, is also what you and I have in common. By leaning into it, we invite ourselves to share its burden.

CLIMATE GRIEF ISN'T SNOWFLAKE—IT'S BADASS

When it comes to climate grief, the default is to shy away from these difficult conversations. Nihilism is the default defense mechanism of the twenty-first century when it comes to climate angst. In Dr. Atkinson's words, "openly facing up to the issues that are weighing you down or keeping you up at night is the most effective remedy."

She also finds it ironic her students were getting attacked for being snowflakes because it takes so much courage to confront issues directly.

"Hiding your head in the sand and retreating into denial or cynicism…that's the easy path. These students are taking the hard route."

* * *

THREE TAKEAWAY LESSONS ON ECO-ANXIETY:
1. Climate change is not "going" to happen. It's happening now.
2. It takes courage to confront anger and anxiety toward what we're losing on this planet.
3. Loss is powerful because it is universal.

My biggest takeaway from Dr. Atkinson was the latter. You can try to shoo away data or statistics, but there is no denying someone else's grief. It is impossible to even quantify grief, and yet, it is a sentiment we all share and can relate to. The thought of losing family members, losing a home, or losing a favorite animal to a natural disaster is universally horrifying regardless of opinions on climate change.

To deal with the stress and burden of the climate crisis, Dr. Atkinson runs. After a really bad spell of mass extinction news several years ago, she headed out for a run only to find that it was difficult to breathe due to smoke levels from historical wildfires. Ironically, it was climate change that took away her best form of climate therapy that summer.

And she's not alone.

"With so many other colleagues and students who hike or backcountry ski in the mountains to get away from the despair of their climate research—but there's a lack of snow and dying trees up there—it's just another reminder of what we're trying to escape," she explains.

Still, Dr. Atkinson left me with an important message.

"I think that that kind of inescapability of it reminds us that, in a certain sense, we're still fighting, but we also have to learn to accept and adapt. Because if we don't, then the places that provide solace and therapy to us [...] aren't going to change, and we have to learn to still love them in these altered states."

And that lesson, learning to love the Earth in its altered states, might be the most challenging for future generations to tackle. Until then, we can search for unity in loss.

People like Dr. Atkinson might just help us find it.

PART THREE

HOW TO TALK ~~TO~~ WITH OTHERS ABOUT CLIMATE CHANGE

CHAPTER 11

KNOW YOUR AUDIENCE

The unexpected action of deep listening can create a space of transformation capable of shattering complacency and despair.

—TERRY TEMPEST WILLIAMS

It's the first rule of giving any good presentation: Know your audience.

So frequently does this piece of advice come up in marketing, scriptwriting, and corporate presentations that a lot of people think of it as a buzzword phrase, brushing it off by merely acknowledging who your audience *is* and predicting how well your talking at them might go for your own sake. Knowing your audience is more than being aware that your audience exists or being aware of how receptive they may or may not be to the message you are sharing with them. In other words, it's more than surviving the presentation!

Say you're volunteering for a local chapter of a climate advocacy group in your hometown. You've been asked to go speak about climate change in three separate events: a college campus guest lecture, a retirement home, and a garden club. What's your message on climate change? Does it change as you prepare to speak in front of each group? Central message aside, the reality of science communication is that if your *presentation* follows the same script for all three audiences, your message is dead on arrival.

Elliott, one of the friends I work with in Citizens' Climate Lobby, did something remarkable this year. He announced to a small group of us in the Duke chapter that he had arranged a meeting with the leaders and executive board members of both Young Americans for Liberty (a libertarian group) and Duke College Republicans on campus to discuss climate change. We bore no ill will toward any of them, but upon hearing Elliott's plan, I heard a chorus of chuckles, some members capitulating to the most practical reaction and just shaking their heads while murmuring a resigned "good luck."

Sure enough, Elliott disappeared the next evening. While I didn't expect him to spark any of their interest in climate, I had faith that, at the very least, he wouldn't spur any sort of physical combat in the meeting room. He radiated quite the opposite in his happy-go-lucky demeanor, and he seemed like he usually had a plan to "know his audience" going into tougher climate conversations.

The next day, we learned that by the end of the meeting, everyone in the room was open to attending the next Citizens Climate Lobby Meeting.

It was safe to say we were awestruck—not because we doubted the open-mindedness of these group executives—but because it would be rare to see a group of adult policymakers reach a similar place of common ground after 1.5 hours of conversation.

Elliott understood and respected the fact that he'd be talking with strong libertarians who were very skeptical of government intervention, and he chose to focus more on discussing the Energy Innovation and Carbon Dividend Act (H.R. 763) itself as a potential market-based solution, rather than a solely theoretical discussion debating the causes and implications of climate change.[119] Compromise is written into the framework of the bill itself; while carbon polluters (fossil fuel companies) would pay a price for emitting their carbon, that price rises *gradually*, excludes the military and agricultural sector, charges the average American nothing for individual carbon habits (a "Polluters Pay" model), and includes a regulatory pause for fossil fuel companies as they adjust to carbon pricing.[120]

In Elliott's words, his three key takeaways from his successful meeting were:

- **Listen**: Really seek to understand what people's priorities are and why
- **Know your information**: Mentioning the Obama-era U.S.-China climate agreement or *Juliana v. United States* climate case helped build credibility and add depth to conversations

---

119 U.S. Congress, House, Energy Innovation and Carbon Dividend Act of 2019, HR 763, 116th Cong., 1st sess., introduced in House January 24, 2019.

120 Ibid.

- **There is more than meets the eye**: The fact that someone who doesn't believe government should exist became willing to attend a Citizens' Climate Lobby meeting emphasizes the value of spending time engaging. People's initial thoughts may not reflect the full range of options they'd be open to.

And Elliott told me specifically that he'd like to *avoid* jumping to the following conclusions:

- He somehow "changed their minds."
- He "convinced them he was right."
- He "opened their eyes" to some truth.

Instead, he had found a way to build off the group executives' pre-existing open-mindedness, respect them for it, and reach the conclusion that young conservatives, climate lobbyists, and Libertarians actually all care about the planet in their own ways. They were interested in hearing more about market-based solutions and presented some of their own, including one strategy of individual and class-action lawsuits against fossil fuel companies.

"It really speaks to the idea of treating everybody as an ally or an ally that doesn't know it yet," he told me.

I had always been skeptical of the phrase "ally that doesn't know it yet," as I thought it sounded borderline dogmatic. However, I didn't realize that an "ally" doesn't have to agree with 100 percent of the things you say. One of my law professors always used to tell me, "Don't let the perfect be the enemy of the good"—and that's true of any negotiation.

LESSONS FROM A SCIENCE COMMUNICATOR

I also interviewed Dr. Jory Weintraub, one of my favorite professors, to get a better sense of what it really means to know your audience. I had met Jory over a year ago in a course he taught called "Science and Pop Culture" (which was exactly as geeky and amazing as it sounds), and it was in that class that I first learned the know-your-audience rule. In addition to teaching, Jory is the science communication director with the Duke Initiative for Science and Society.

Jory is the kind of professor who radiates a contagious passion for his subject. During the semester, he frequently invited all of his classes to science cafe conversations in the area, emailed us relevant articles outside of class, and even encouraged two students in our class to deliver a presentation about the influence of science memes on Facebook. He, himself, defies any traditional assumptions someone might have about a science professor; he often wears band t-shirts rather than a coat and tie, opens every class with jokes rather than jargon, and invites us to call him "Jory" rather than "Doctor." Instead of listing off his scientific credentials, he first introduced himself to the class as a fifty-something-year-old father who used to go to school with Robert Downey, Jr. and play in a punk rock band.

But Jory is an expert. A seasoned science communicator, he has gone into classrooms, community centers, museums, and town halls, engaging the public directly on topics ranging from evolution to climate change to simply what it means to be a scientist. He had started off as a biologist by training, with an undergraduate degree in biochemistry and a PhD in immunology, but admitted he never planned on staying in research. He was far more interested in science education, diversity, and inclusion of underrepresented groups in STEM disciplines, as well as science outreach, which was the focus of his post-doctoral fellowship. "And here I am, twenty years later," he told me with a smile.

Science communication often involves a learn-by-doing approach. For Jory, it was a ten-year adventure he spent traveling across the country and the world, tackling the difficult task of teaching evolution in areas where it was historically not accepted or embraced. Accompanied by a team of graduate or post-doc students, he traveled everywhere from the bayous of Louisiana to the Ozark Mountains, in front of audiences ranging from a prison school in West Virginia to a mental hospital in Massachusetts. Certainly, part of the team's goal was to bring evolution into these unique settings, but their underlying goal was much simpler: to humanize science.

"Part of [our goal] was to reach really underserved areas or institutions where scientists didn't typically go and just expose students not only to evolution, but also to science in general. And, because we were targeting small rural communities and really out-of-the-way places, a lot of times what we heard from the students and the teachers is that we were the first scientists they had ever met in their lives. [We visited] high school seniors who had never met a scientist before, let alone an evolutionary biologist. And so, part of the goal is to humanize evolution and science in general and give kids who have an interest in science an opportunity to meet real scientists."

A big part of this is intersectionality and diversity. How can you know and connect with your audience when they aren't given fair representation in your discipline? For instance, scientific fields like ecology, behavioral science, and evolutionary biology have historically tended to be very white disciplines, lacking the voices and expertise of minorities and people of color. Forty percent of black adults employed in STEM fields say their race or ethnicity has made it harder for them to succeed, according to a 2018 study.[121]

To promote diversity in STEM, Jory made sure his team of communicators represented a diverse range of backgrounds (so "it wasn't all people that looked like me," he assured me) and women, people of color, and younger scientists really pioneered this outreach. Together, they would reach out to K-12 students and say, "I am what a scientist looks like today, and you can join this field too." Those words resonate more profoundly than ever in the climate movement, especially for young people who will grow up to take the place of the climate scientists on the front lines today. Gen Z's values of intersectionality and personal identity play an important role in audience outreach.

TRUST BEFORE TEACHING
Another key takeaway: Make an effort to connect with your audience on a human level before jumping right into the topic—especially if it's controversial.

---

121 Cary Funk and Kim Parker, "Racial Diversity and Discrimination in the U.S. STEM Workforce," *Pew Research Center's Social & Demographic Trends Project*, January 9, 2018.

"If I were to go into a town hall in Louisiana to talk about evolution, and I walked in there, and the first words out of my mouth were 'Today, I'm going to tell you why evolution is a real thing and why you're wrong if you don't believe in it,' I'm not going to win any friends that way. People are going to shut down; they're going to close off their minds to what I have to say."

Any time you go into a new environment or venue to a new (and potentially reluctant) audience, a good rule of thumb is to try to connect with them on something that has nothing to do with that discipline. Jory discovered this not only through research but also experientially through his traveling. He cited another example from Missouri, a state that has historically resisted the teaching of evolution.

"If I were going to Missouri [...] I would start by talking about how great it was when Kansas City won the Super Bowl yesterday—something that I know they're going to be excited about and willing to embrace. What's that going to do? It's going to humanize me. So, instead of this scary academic guy who comes from an East Coast elite university to talk about something they don't believe in, I'm a football fan."

And if you fail to reach an understanding with your audience on the science? You've at least connected with them on a personal level and had a positive interaction. The most reluctant audience member might say, "I'm still not concerned about climate change, evolution, or vaccinations (you name it), but that guy didn't seem so bad. Maybe scientists/scholars/activists aren't as bad as I thought."

By assembling a diverse team of presenters, you ensure someone on your team will have an inherent connection or similarity to your audience. And that's a powerful starting point. Rather than speaking about evolution as an agnostic-atheist onstage solo, Jory would always bring a second person—a person of faith or a minister—to completely shift the paradigm that evolution and faith are incompatible. "They're hearing from *me*, but they're also hearing from someone who's very aligned with their ideology, and who they trust inherently because of what that person represents. And that's going to make them much more receptive to what I have to say," Jory affirms. You could have the most wonderful talk prepared but still get mentally blocked out from the beginning if you don't create ways to connect with your audience. Building trust before teaching, even slowly or incrementally, is the first step.

KNOW—AND BECOME—YOUR AUDIENCE

The next step is to step into the shoes of your audience. We'll go over this more in Chapter 13, but the bottom line is to identify what your audience's stumbling blocks are that prevent them from aligning with you ideologically. What are their concerns? Where are they coming from? Often, you'll realize it's a completely reasonable place.

For evolution, the stumbling block is usually religion and the idea that faith and evolution are incompatible.

For climate change, a variety of stumbling blocks exist. The economy, and the idea that environmental regulation and economic growth are incompatible, is one of them. Another one is socioeconomic status and culture; if you work for automotive manufacturers or have worked in your hometown's coal industry for ten generations, you're more likely to downplay climate change or reject most proposed solutions. And the key is to recognize the validity of that! Wouldn't you feel the same way if your livelihood or identity felt threatened? Rather than preaching about enviro-guilt, pointing fingers, or villainizing the fossil fuel industry, consider focusing on *training* and *career transitions* from fossil fuel industry jobs to green technology jobs. Or, as Elliott did, take time to ask for your audience's ideal solutions. This tip is especially important when communicating between older and younger generations.

Research the following demographics of your audience:

- Age
- Education
- Background
- Socioeconomic status
- Geographical location
- Interests
- Motives

How might these identities lead to stumbling blocks for your audience? Identify the biggest stumbling block and focus on *that* in your conversation, rather than preparing a general spiel on climate.

Another stumbling block to focus on is where your audience falls on what could be called the "spectrum of engagement." The Yale Program on Climate Change Communication ran a study on how Americans engage on climate change and came up with a fascinating project titled "Global Warming's Six Americas," sorting Americans into six broad categories [122]:

Alarmed → Concerned → Cautious → Disengaged → Doubtful → Dismissive

The project breaks down each category as follows:

"The **Alarmed** are fully convinced of the reality and seriousness of climate change and are already taking individual, consumer, and political action to address it. The **Concerned** are also convinced that global warming is happening and a serious problem but have not yet engaged the issue personally. Three other Americas—the **Cautious**, the **Disengaged**, and the **Doubtful**—represent different stages of understanding and acceptance of the problem, and none are actively involved. The final America—the **Dismissive**—are very sure it is not happening and are actively involved as opponents of a national effort to reduce greenhouse gas emissions."[123]

For that last category, the moment that always comes to mind is when President Donald Trump polled the audience at one of his rallies on climate change. "Who believes in global warming? Wow, not much huh?" To Trump's credit, he clearly knew his audience. Unsurprisingly, few hands shot up, as it is perhaps most convenient to assume the "Dismissive"

---

122 Anthony Leiserowitz, Edward Maibach, and Connie Roser-Renouf, "Global Warming's Six Americas," *Yale Program on Climate Change Communication*, 2009–2020.

123 Ibid.

attitude as a way to avoid devoting any time to discussing climate solutions in the first place.

But, as it turns out, most Americans are not actually denialists or diehard believers. In fact, although the "Alarmed" category is at an encouraging all-time high of 31 percent (as of November 2019), 59 percent of Americans still fall somewhere between "Concerned" and "Doubtful."[124] If you think about it, neither extreme should absorb all of your time; the "Alarmed" have already been reached, and the "Dismissive" may require longer-term discourse and trust-building before they're able to acknowledge climate change conceptually. Knowing your audience will likely fall somewhere in the "worried middle," as some communicators call it, means you're better off discussing actionable solutions that address your audience's stumbling blocks.

The last thing to remember is to avoid sorting entire generations into any one category of Global Warming's Six Americas. Not all boomers are dismissive and not all Gen Zers are alarmed— chances are, you've met folks of all different ages across that helpful continuum.

CHALLENGES IN OUTREACH

I later asked Jory what he thought the biggest challenges are in science communication and outreach.

---

124 Matthew Goldberg et al., "For the First Time, the Alarmed Are Now the Largest of Global Warming's Six Americas," *Yale Program on Climate Change Communication*, 2020.

"So many challenges," he muttered under his breath.

First, he mentioned hyperpolarization. Discussing controversial topics is hard today when so many people bring their own biases into different conversations. Second, budgetary concerns: "Science journalism is becoming very challenged in the field because newspapers and news sources are cutting budgets and slashing back on their coverage of science," he explained, making it more difficult to *have* an audience in the first place. Finally, he mentioned the challenge of "who does it," which entails recognizing who the scientists and trained science communicators are. Unfortunately, finding an overlap between the two is rare.

The positive side of that, he told me, is that the archetype of a traditional "scientist" is changing.

"More and more people who are trained as scientists, such as myself, are starting to veer away from the traditional path of becoming a professor and running a lab, and more and more people are starting to pursue what is sometimes referred to as alternative science career paths—such as science communication."

I remember one of our Science and Pop Culture classes had focused on the portrayal of science—and scientists—in movies throughout history. We see white lab coats. Total lack of social skills. An ivory tower of either a tube-filled laboratory or a cluster of computers in their parents' basement. Even the "mad scientist" archetype, over time, distanced scientists from the public rather subconsciously. Most people today do trust medical and climate scientists a fair amount, but less than a third of people report a "great deal" of confidence in any of these groups to act in the public interest.[125]

Growing up, it was also unfortunate to see scientists so frequently portrayed in the media as boring side characters who always tried to explain their findings in fervor until they were told to "skip it over and get to the good part" for the protagonist. In today's world, scientists are the protagonists. And thanks to people like Jory, younger generations are growing up with that epiphany.

LEARNING TO DEPOLARIZE...YOURSELF
The final piece of advice I'd offer on reaching your audience is to start by depolarizing yourself in advance.

I recently attended a self-depolarization workshop, partially on a whim to get off campus, that took place in my community. There are few moments as mundane as a two-hour workshop on a Saturday morning that I would deem "lifechanging," but this is one of them.

At the time, I didn't fully understand what "depolarization" entailed. Did it mean abandoning all my personal beliefs? Did it mean flipping a switch and shutting up about politics altogether? Part of me was worried that attending would somehow dilute all my personal worldviews into a neutral and agreeable grayscale.

---

125 Cary Funk, "Mixed Messages about Public Trust in Science," *Issues in Science and Technology*, Pew Research Center, December 8, 2017.

None of these proved to be the case. We all took surveys ranking our own levels of anger and disillusionment with people or ideas on the other end of the political spectrum, then spent the next two hours learning how to separate the supporters from their ideologies, pledge to only dispute the latter, and pivot away from harmful conversations that just slam and personally attack people who vote differently from you. What's special about depolarization exercises is that you come out feeling like a new person, as if you have a renewed purpose as a peacemaker in everyday encounters.

What I will never forget about the workshop is that it was *packed*—I mean absolutely jammed up with people—and most of them were above the age of fifty. I had fully expected the workshop to be a couple of college kids and millennials, perhaps because I was buying into the flawed assumption that older generations are more fixed in their political affiliations and behaviors. Nope, the room was a mix. One middle-aged woman sitting behind me had a bold streak of blue in her hair and had brought along two of her kids. In front of me sat a sixteen or seventeen-year-old genius who had evidently brought along his two parents. The high levels of both attendance and enthusiastic participation showcased the sheer willingness of adults to raise their families on this beautiful new concept of depolarization.

* * *

KNOW YOUR AUDIENCE: TAKEAWAYS

1. **Do your research**: What sources does this audience consult? Who are their thought leaders throughout history? What are their values?

2. **Go in with the right mindset**: Do not belittle your audience or assume you're there to convert them. Going in with "I'm going to change all these people's minds" is the wrong approach!

3. **Respect your audience**: Put yourself in their shoes, appreciate their willingness to be there, and use that respect as a baseline.

4. **Humanize yourself**: Use the beginning to connect with your audience on an issue unrelated to the environment.

5. **Identify "stumbling blocks"** on the issue of climate change or climate activism for your particular audience.

6. **Highlight the compromises** that will come out of a proposed environmental action by tapping into shared group identities.

7. **Listen:** Use the time to ask your audience questions, find out their ideal solutions, and learn from them. Now is your chance!

I reflected on my conversation with Jory for a few days afterward. I kept thinking of something he said toward the very end. The difference between the two of us, he said, is that "you, Joy, are idealistic and won't stop fighting."

Jory assured me he's still in the fight too but added that a big part of him has also grown admittedly cynical from having witnessed a lifetime of injustice, corporate greed, and those in power fighting harder to preserve the status quo. Youth like Greta Thunberg offer him a source of hope, but the stamina to cling to that hope falters with each passing decade.

In all of my research on different generations' treatment of the environment, I hadn't even considered the thought that some of the older scientists and activists, who may actually care the most, are slowed by a sinister force that my generation has yet to face: the disillusionment that comes with age. It's not "giving up"—it's simply the ideological exhaustion accompanying decades of fighting the good fight.

The question is whether the idealism, the beauty, and the passion of people like Greta is strong enough to overcome the overwhelming power, the oldest forms of wealth, and the injustice that still persists in the status quo.

The beauty of youth, in Jory's words, is believing the answer to that question is yes.

"You gotta hang on to that idealism as long as you can," he assured me, looking out at the gothic spires behind us. "Find what you're passionate about and do what makes you feel like you're making the biggest difference."

For him, it's science communication—but also homelessness. I was touched to learn that, on top of all his global-scale outreach, he's spent the past twenty-five years volunteering as a cook at a homeless shelter.

"It's easy to just sit around pissed and complain and rail on things," he shrugged. I laughed out of agreement and nervous self-awareness. "But at the end of the day, how am I making the world a better place?"

He paused. "I've never made a big change politically; I've had one vote. That's all I've ever had. But I've made thousands of meals for homeless people."

I've thought about those words for a long time. His words put the two-part mantra "think globally, act locally" into perspective (especially because my generation tends to infatuate ourselves solely with the former part). But this is only the beginning of what different generations can learn from one another. As long as young activists keep our sense of global idealism, Jory promised there will always be a few old people like him—his words, not mine—who are willing to listen, stand, and fight alongside us.

The question of whether younger generations should ever be *criticized* for our determined idealism roiled in the back of my mind. But Jory just shook his head.

"Stay in that place as long as you can."

CHAPTER 12

KNOW YOUR FACTS

———

At the heart of science is an essential balance between two
seemingly contradictory attitudes—an openness to new ideas,
no matter how bizarre or counterintuitive they may be, and
the most ruthless skeptical scrutiny of all ideas, old and new.
This is how deep truths are winnowed from deep nonsense.

—CARL SAGAN

THE DREADED DINNER TABLE

Your extended family of twelve sit around the Thanksgiving
dinner table.

Grandparents, aunts, uncles, parents, children, and distant relatives have all come together for a time of gratitude,
togetherness, and inevitable bickering about political matters
that results from spending prolonged periods of time waiting
to eat while in that state of togetherness. The dreaded dinner
table tension begins.

"Human beings are not responsible for climate change!" declares That One Relative, probably after realizing with horror that, for the first time in family history, this year's turkey meat had been joined by a climate-friendly, plant-based alternative option, Tofurky.

Dare you speak up?

You briefly explain the greenhouse effect and point out that carbon dioxide levels in the atmosphere fluctuate closely with temperature, and both have been in extremes never observed for millennia since the Industrial Revolution, when humans burned fossil fuels on a large scale.[126] You add that, graphically, carbon dioxide levels were relatively steady (averaging 230 parts per million) for 2.5 million years and then visibly spiked to where they are today (over 410 parts per million).[127]

"So, there is actually a nearly-unanimous consensus of climate scientists today who have concluded the opposite of that statement and are telling us the planet is warming due to anthropogenic greenhouse gas emissions," you reply.

"But the climate has been changing for hundreds of thousands of years," the relative argues.

"Okay, how did you get the data that helps you know that?" you ask.

---

126 Jiawei Da, Yi Ge Zhang, Gen Li, Xianqiang Meng, and Junfeng Ji, "Low CO2 Levels of the Entire Pleistocene Epoch." *Nature Communications* 10, no.1(2009): 1–9

127 Ibid.

"Climate scientists," they reply.

You shrug politely. "Well, guess what those very climate scientists are telling us right now."

* * *

The conversation above is entirely fictional and probably a little more sassy than necessary for the civil discourse I otherwise endorse in this book. This pattern is actually inspired by a workshop held at Duke called "How to Talk to Your Relatives About Climate Change," conveniently held right before Thanksgiving. It was one of my professors who suggested the mic-dropping line at the end as an appropriate response to the "natural climate fluctuation" argument.

YOUR FACT ARSENAL

How can we take all of the common values we discussed in the previous seven chapters and consolidate them into an understandable, accessible arsenal of knowledge?

Part of growing up in the grassroots during any era is understanding that conversations like the one above are going to arise more and more during adulthood. Among most crucial pieces of environmental communication between generations, or between anyone, is to have enough familiarity with the relevant facts and data of climate change that you can calmly and confidently defend your worldviews (or Thanksgiving dinner choices) with them. In other words, it helps to have the feeling that you are "on your toes" with the basics. In addition to the resources in the Introduction, there is great general information on climate change within the following sources:

- Climate.nasa.gov: This site is great for imagery, visualizations, and a logical breakdown of easy-to-follow facts. Plus, everyone loves NASA.[128]
- The Yale Program on Climate Change Communication: This source studies public attitudes, highlighting what works and what doesn't work. It is used copiously in this book for a reason. (Climatecommunication.yale.edu)[129]
- SkepticalScience.com: A great starting place for debunking each and every climate myth with peer-reviewed article evidence, broken down by argument. ("Skepticism is a process; denial is a position.")[130]
- As mentioned in the Introduction:
  - Intergovernmental Panel on Climate Change (IPCC),
  - the National Academies of Science, and
  - the National Oceanic and Atmospheric Administration (NOAA).
- *Drawdown*: This book is for solution-oriented folks. It offers one hundred practical, research-informed approaches to curbing the worst of climate change, at your fingertips.[131] (Alternatively, see drawdown.org for the Table of Solutions broken down by sector.)

---

128 "Global Climate Change: Vital Signs of the Planet," NASA Jet Propulsion Laboratory website.

129 "Yale Program on Climate Change Communication," website homepage.

130 . "Skeptical Science: Getting Skeptical About Global Warming Skepticism," website homepage.

131 Paul Hawken, ed., *Drawdown: The Most Comprehensive Plan Ever Proposed to Reverse Global Warming* (New York: Penguin Books, 2017).

This is not to say you need to read the latest IPCC report or 1,656-page National Climate Assessment cover to cover and quote it like scripture in everyday conversations. But it might be helpful to refresh on the basics. Once you know your audience and determine the most relevant and helpful information to work with them, even just a fact sheet's worth of understanding will help you communicate.

The facts might not even be scientific—I once worked with a lobbyist who framed a carbon pricing bill solely in the lens of job creation and economic statistics. He had conducted his research and realized that listing facts about pollution and particulates just wouldn't land with that senator. He was right; economic statistics instead proved to be the most powerful. (2.4 million jobs could be created!) Similarly, I like to justify a low-carbon lifestyle simply with facts about how much money it saves, i.e. I was able to cut my grocery bill down by one-third this past summer by eating plant-based foods.

After a while, your "arsenal" of facts will feel less like an arsenal (maybe a little too combative of a connotation) and instead feel more like a dynamic pool of knowledge you can draw from comfortably.

TIPS, TRICKS, AND MENTAL MODELS
Years of classes and training in environmental communication have left me restlessly trying to construct a "master list" of climate facts. However, realizing the difficulty of condensing decades worth of important data into a fact sheet that

likely already exists on NASA's or NOAA's website, I came up with more of a strategic framework instead.

Below is my personal list of the tips I use when building factual arguments:

1. **Know your audience.**
2. **Pick your sources** from peer-reviewed, minimally biased, and transparent databases. The best way to do this is the old-fashioned way: visit a library and sit down with a library research assistant. This will cut your search time in half!
3. **Speak in real terms**: Avoid eco-clichés, empty hyperboles, and media greenwashing. Telling conservative members of Congress to "go green" or recycle will get you nowhere. Solely pleading that "the world is on fire" will get you nowhere if you don't tell a compelling story with data on Australia, the Amazon, and our own West Coast wildfires.
4. **Balance facts with sentimental appeals**: Infuse personal stories with economic, sociopolitical, and scientific information. Shoot for action-sized pieces.
5. **Anticipate counterarguments** and craft your arsenal of facts accordingly. Making a physical list of the concerns your audience might have can help you respond to them on your feet. It's like in ninth grade debate all over again!
6. **Don't make up the answers**: If you don't know the answer to something, don't pretend to—the integrity of science rests on admitting uncertainty.
7. **Familiarize yourself with generational talking points**: How have other generations handled wicked problems in the past?
8. **Make an effort to be practical, logical, and sincere.**

With all of these in mind, the next step is to evaluate your own mental model.

A mental model is essentially the way a person interprets the world, usually founded in past experiences and less-than-complete facts. So, very subjective. I like to picture mental models like funnels, filtering through the information we're exposed to rather selectively. I would also compare it to that one all-nighter you pulled on an essay in ninth grade where, instead of conducting a proper literature review, any—and every—piece of information you found would be desperately crafted to fit a preconceived thesis you somehow already had in the back of your mind. Mental models come down to our deepest biases, and they determine what we pay attention to and how we approach problems.

The Center for Research on Environmental Decisions (CRED) offers a great example in the way people interpret temperature swings:

Both believers and skeptics find it tempting to over-interpret short-term hot or cold swings in temperature as evidence for or against climate change. Such confirmation bias in action can lead people who believe that climate change equals warmer temperatures to pay greater attention to supportive data, interpreting a heat wave in the Great Lakes region, for example, as evidence that their mental model is correct. Skeptics of climate

change might pay more attention to news that
announces close-to-normal levels of polar sea
ice, a momentary finding but one that fits their
mental model and enables them to disregard the
more scientifically relevant trend of dramatic
loss of sea ice in the Arctic and 'debunk' climate
change. Both sides will either ignore facts that
contradict their mental model of climate change
or interpret them as exceptions to the rule.[132]

This would explain why, in the words of one of my professors, *fact bombardment leads to entrenchment.* When we hear something that clashes slightly with our mental model or personal beliefs, those beliefs actually become more ingrained; our reflex is to dig our feet even further into the ground and forcefully reason the new information into the pegs of our preferred mental model. If someone's favorite celebrity (or politician) is caught causing trouble, the fan's first instinct is not "What did she do?" but "She was *framed!*"

In a more relevant example proposed by researcher Anthony Leiserowitz, if someone has incorrectly assumed the ozone hole is synonymous to climate change, they may assume we are dealing with a "hole" in the "greenhouse" and suggest inaccurate solutions, such as banning physical aerosol cans

---

132 The Psychology of Climate Change Communication," Center for Research on Environmental Decisions.

themselves.[133] There is no bad intention behind the reasoning of this mental model, but it unfortunately leads to solutions that, well, just wouldn't work.

Luckily, people can correct their mental models by re-synthesizing information. In order for new climate change information to go over well, communicators should be familiar with common misconceptions and have a game plan for replacing them with correct information. But remember—you can't reach in and change another person's mental model; they must choose to change it! The best you can do is guide them to a place where they can voluntarily reach their own accurate conclusions about climate change.

* * *

And climate change communication strategies are changing for grassroots activists. Outright climate denial is dwindling—which is great—except it's being replaced by the hopeless, almost-cynical paralysis that arises from feeling disconnected from climate change.

Katherine Hayhoe, an atmospheric scientist who co-authored the National Climate Assessment, managed to boil down the report itself into a single statement:

Climate change is impacting everyone now.

---

133 Ibid.

Her three biggest takeaways are as follows:[134]

1. There are already climate refugees in the United States.
2. Hurricanes are getting stronger, bigger, and slower, meaning they can sit over us for longer.
3. Climate change hits us in the Achilles' heel.

(For the latter point, she compared peering into a climate-changed future to looking into a funhouse mirror: All your worst features are accentuated.) Hayhoe's three takeaways are more important than ever in selecting the right facts to close the conceptual distance of climate change. Outright climate change denial isn't our real enemy—it's the idea that "global warming does not matter to me."

THE BIG SHIFT: MOVING PAST POLAR BEARS

During the 2000s and 2010s, what got people's attention on climate change were pictures of sad-looking polar bears stranded on icebergs. Admittedly, these pictures are heartbreaking. But what's even more heartbreaking is the disconnect that surrounds them. The imperiled polar bears, coral reefs, shellfish plunging toward extinction, swaths of rainforest, and even communities of people, are perceived as *too distant* to spur the average American into wartime or pandemic levels of action; they are seen as slow and intangible casualties of a force "too simple and too huge" to collectively brace against.

---

134 Greta Moran, "1,656 Pages Too Long? Climate Report Coauthor Katharine Hayhoe Has 3 Takeaways," *Grist,* November 27, 2018.

Our salvation over the next century will be showing that climate change is happening right now and impacting human well-being. Know your facts about how everyone will be affected, especially our most vulnerable and voiceless communities.

Former EPA Chief Gina McCarthy pioneered this idea of human-centric and environmental justice-centric climate thinking.

> *"Climate change is not about polar bears, which I think are cute...**it's about people.** It's about water, wastewater, and the infrastructure that is under our water. It's about the sewers that are backing up and overflowing all at the same time. It's about our drinking water supplies."*[135]

And in a world that also watched environmental justice horrors unfold in Flint, Michigan, and in Parkersburg, West Virginia, I think McCarthy is exactly right. The fossil fuel industry is willing to go to the same lengths to continue indiscriminately emitting greenhouse gases into the atmosphere as chemical companies are to continue discharging toxic PFAS from a point source into local waterways.

I recently watched the movie *Dark Waters*, a true story starring Mark Ruffalo as Rob Bilott, a Dow Chemical lawyer who

---

135 Brentin Mock, "Message from the EPA: It's about Protecting People, Not Polar Bears," *Grist*, September 23, 2013.

witnessed and fought against his own industry as it knowingly poisoned the town of Parkersburg, armored by skilled lawyers, expensive cover-ups, and the spread of disinformation. There is a haunting scene in which Bilott drives past a young girl biking past with an odd smile, only to realize her teeth had turned completely black due to PFAS residue in the town's water supply. He manages to bring justice to Parkersburg by locking himself in a room and poring over Dow's files for days on end, collecting evidence and connecting the dots until his case is irrefutable. Bilott epitomizes the power of knowing your facts. *Dark Waters* is a story every American should watch for a taste of what it feels like to be furious at environmental injustice. No matter the scale, is "economic feasibility" an issue when people are being poisoned?

The health effects of climate change are equally horrifying. The World Health Organization projects that between 2030 and 2050, climate change will cause approximately 250,000 additional deaths every year from heat stress, malnutrition, diarrhea, and malaria.[136] That's enough of an estimate for most of us to care. But for people who speak solely in economic terms, the report also finds that health costs will total between $2 billion to $4 billion *every year*.[137] And if you're speaking with someone who refuses to think globally, until you teach them to do so, you may also assert that climate change is happening *now* in the United States. Coastal residents are already losing their lives in extreme flooding and

---

136 "Climate Change and Health," World Health Organization, February 1, 2018.

137 Ibid.

Hundred-Year Hurricane events which, in my home of North Carolina, we seem to ironically brace for on a yearly basis.

Low-income and minority communities suffer disproportionately as nearby commercial hog lagoons flood wastewater onto their property. While air pollution endangers healthy lung development in children and adolescents, larger changes in air quality (from pollution, prolonged heat waves, forest fires, floods, and droughts) have a "quantifiable impact" on both the disease rate and the death rate of respiratory diseases like asthma.[138] The most vulnerable age-group populations in the United States are young children, pregnant mothers, and the elderly, providing a perfect enough multigenerational cross-section for us to join forces on the latest battlefront of climate justice: human health.

Because health, justice, and equality rest upon the fulcrum of sound science, thousands of other university students and I have decided to pursue STEM degrees. Our decision has already entailed many hours of studying and coffee-fueled all-nighters on problem sets, but the prospect of serving society through science—like so many older role models in our life already have—drives us to carry that torch.

THE MARCH FOR SCIENCE
One spring morning in 2017, I attended the March for Science in D.C. with my dad.

---

138 Gerrano D'Amato et al., "Effects on Asthma and Respiratory Allergy of Climate Change and Air Pollution." *Multidisciplinary Respiratory Medicine* 10, no. 1 (2015): 39.

The March for Science is exactly what it sounds like: simply defending science and advocating for evidence-based reasoning in today's policymaking. Making sure scientists and experts have a voice. Defending factuality.

Several aspects of the march really stuck out to me, one of which was how packed it was. Thousands of people lined the streets in what had started as a grassroots Facebook event scheduled for Earth Day. I turned to my dad and commented that I got a really strong "teacher vibe" from the attendees; many were between the ages of thirty and sixty, wearing shirts with chemistry puns or galactic collages of Bill Nye's and Neil DeGrasse Tyson's faces, several signs depicting everything from evolutionary phylogenies to Keeling Curves. *I'm here for my students*, a few signs read. They were Gen Xers and boomers, and they seemed ready to die for this cause. The attendance was a mix of ages and backgrounds, yet the majority of attendees seemed to have had a lifelong stake in science, whether as a career, as a fascination, or as a discipline they hoped to preserve in its purest form for their children.

It's hard for me to antagonize older generations after having seen so many Gen X and boomer-aged activists, many of whom I learned were highly respected scientists in their fields, give their entire day to such a systemic and future-oriented cause. It is thanks to those generations of scientists that we have a consensus status of 97–99 percent on anthropogenic climate change.[139] It was those activists who surged ahead to walk behind the banner and to speak behind the podium.

139 John Cook et al., "Quantifying the Consensus on Anthropogenic Global Warming in the Scientific Literature," *Environmental Research Letters* 8,

After we began walking, I started paying attention to the messaging on people's signs and banners. How many of them showcased statistics? How many idolized historical scientists, and how many of them plead for policy change? I was on the lookout for unique call-to-action methods—in a sense, gauging the temperature on the state of modern science communication.

Of course, there were also a couple of signs and activist groups that directly bashed Trump. This was another aspect of the march I distinctly remember. His massive orange caricature towered over the sea of people on posters, in meticulously crafted sculptures, and even in lifelike costumes. I've hopped on the red line and Metroed into D.C. enough times to realize you're going to find overt anti-Trumpism in pretty much any theme of march, ranging from the Women's March, to the March for Our Lives, to any Climate March, to the Animal Rights March. But it felt odd, in that moment, because Trump himself had become a symbol antithetical to Bill Nye the Science Guy, to the little atom logo that had come to emblemize the march on people's t-shirts, and to science itself. It was impossible not to witness the entanglement of science and politics…but what used to be a diplomatic interplay between the two has, in this decade, seemed to devolve into a binary war.

It's hard to know your facts when factuality itself has become a battlefield. (In a time when it seems anyone can handpick their preferred bouquet of facts and news sources, perhaps it would be better to more concretely say know *the* facts.) "Fake

---

no. 2 (2013).

News" and "Alternative Facts," designed to spark polarization, have spread across global media like wildfire. What's even more dangerous about the era of Fake News is that it gives public figures the ability to stamp the term "Fake News" or "hoax" on any information deemed unsavory. Even the current EPA website serves as an example of this, as it falls prey to censorship and oversimplification. Having been purged of vocabulary like "global warming," "greenhouse gases," "fossil fuels," and "science," while also filled with missing links and intentionally confusing site navigation, anti-environmental administrators have undermined decades of scientific research. Heather Zichal, previously President Barack Obama's top White House adviser on energy and climate change, called the Trump Administration's edits to the EPA website "an unprecedented attempt to delete or bury credible scientific information they find politically inconvenient."[140]

"The message they're sending, particularly to young people, is that science doesn't matter," Zichal asserts.

"Don't get me wrong—questioning is fine and good, but when you have overwhelming consensus on something, you concede to that. Undermining science means there is no basis on which to act based on fact, which is dangerous."

Scientific censorship is not only dangerous but cross-generational.

---

140 Laignee Barron, "Here's What the EPA's Website Looks Like After a Year of Climate Change Censorship," *Time*, March 1, 2018.

Today, it's the fossil fuel industry. When my parents and grandparents were growing up, it was the tobacco industry (as discussed in Chapter 3). As concerns grew through the 1950s and 1960s that cigarette smoke was causing cancer, the primary goal of the United States' largest tobacco companies became preserving profits—not protecting the public. Their secondary goals? Avoiding litigation and preventing governmental regulation through:

- The reversal of scientific and popular opinion that environmental tobacco smoke was harmful to health
- The restoration of the social acceptability of smoking.[141]

This approach sounds eerily similar to the strategies not just of fossil fuel companies shrugging off the urgency of climate change, but also of Dow Chemical, Bayer-Monsanto, and today's industry giants shirking liability for blue-collar workers seriously injured, or slowly poisoned, while using their chemical products.

"The industry's strategy does not require winning the debates it manufactures," experts on the tobacco industry's tactics conclude.[142] "It is enough to foster and perpetuate the illusion of controversy in order to muddy the waters around scientific findings that threaten the industry."

---

141 Yussuf Saloojee and Elif Dagli, "Tobacco Industry Tactics for Resisting Public Policy on Health," *Bulletin of the World Health Organization* 78 (July 2000): 902–10.

142 Ibid.

Now, when climate scientists actually have the same degree of certainty that human-caused emissions are changing the climate as they do that cigarette smoking is harmful, I realize why the crowds have gathered in such large and diverse numbers—we refuse to be misinformed any longer.[143]

As I walked down Pennsylvania Avenue with my dad, there was a particular moment when we passed by the Newseum building. Thousands of people filled the street with color and noise. I remembered all my grade-school field trips into that building hunting down old newspaper headlines. In a rather surreal moment, as we marched past the towering stone exterior of the building, we could see the words of the First Amendment, etched in huge letters onto the side of the Newseum, a reminder of our protected right to assemble (and petition the government for a redress of grievances).

The sign I carried myself read:

No science
No evidence
No truth
No democracy.

And something felt right, as if this were democracy speaking on behalf of science, channeling through the grassroots a discipline that is so often silenced in industry and in politics. Never before had I so much hope for science in the world.

---

143 Douglas Fischer, "Climate Risks as Conclusive as Link Between Smoking and Lung Cancer," *Scientific American*, March 19, 2014.

Two hours later, I would hear ten-year-old activist "Little Miss Flint" bring down the house in a charismatic speech with the simple assertion that when governments ignore science, "kids get hurt." Five hours later, I would fall asleep on my dad's shoulder on the Metro. But for the next hour, I just enjoyed walking and speaking with climate-conscious science geeks of all ages. Realizing how it is wrong to declare the boomer generation an outright failure on climate, I felt a sense of security in seeing how adamantly older-aged activists defended science and a sense of solidarity in our shared scientific literacy.

Neil DeGrasse Tyson does a much better job of putting that feeling into words. "If you're scientifically literate, the world looks very different to you, and that understanding empowers you."

And that's a fact.

CHAPTER 13

BE STEMPATHETIC

———

Simplicity, patience, compassion. These three are your greatest treasures. Simple in actions and thoughts, you return to the source of being. Patient with both friends and enemies, you accord with the way things are. Compassionate toward yourself, you reconcile all beings in the world.

—LAO TZU, TAO TE CHING

As a climate activist, it's important to strive for something I refer to as "STEMpathy."

STEMpathy is the idea that—even within Science, Technology, Engineering, Math, and other disciplines as technical as climate science—there is a lot of space for what is *human*. For what science can't answer.

It turns out other people have also coined the term "STEMpathy" within their disciplines: *The New York Times* columnist Thomas Friedman, for example, argued in a speech that humanity and empathy are what set us apart from computers, even in an era when AI computers like Watson are competing against humans (their own creators) on *Jeopardy*.[144]

Humanity, empathy, grief, and joy are just a few examples.

By uniting those x-factor qualities with STEM education in the twenty-first century, students will be equipped with "STEMpathy," a certain hybrid of data-driven and relationship-driven connectivity that "cannot be found in an algorithm."[145]

"Nobody cares what you know, because the Google machine knows everything," Friedman said.

"The faster the world gets, the more everything old and slow matters—the things you can't download."[146]

Many of those things are the core values we discussed in Chapters 4–10, such as family, a place of belonging, spirituality, solidarity, awe, and music. (Well, I suppose you can download music. But you can't download the feeling of being shaken to your core by the powerful or transformative lyrics of a favorite artist.)

---

144 Monica Fuglei, "STEMpathy: Thomas Friedman's Case for Humanity in STEM Education," Resilient Educator.

145 Ibid.

146 Ibid.

I've broken down environmental STEMpathy into five shared emotions:

- A Sense of Awe
- A Sense of Pride
- A Sense of Fear
- A Sense of Humor
- A Sense of Belonging

All of these are intertwined with climate change in some way, and they continue to link generations on the issue.

A SENSE OF AWE

It is a universal emotion to be awed by the natural world, as we've seen in previous chapters of this book. Whether you relate more to the harmonious awe of visiting the Great Barrier Reef or the chaotic awe of John Muir fastening himself to the base of a tree during a windstorm, you've most likely experienced some form of it yourself. My personal favorite is the awakening awe of lying outside under a starry sky.

The seasonal crowds of tourists that pack the Grand Canyon, Niagara Falls, the Redwoods, and other universally appreciated destinations evidence the fact that people *crave* the feeling of sharing awe-inspiring experiences in nature. (Ron Swanson, a fictional character in the hit series *Parks and Recreation* who is firmly anti-government, delivers the famous line, "Crying: acceptable at funerals and the Grand Canyon.")

Even places regarded as less "glamorous," like a local park, can inspire awe. After spending enough time in them and learning about the ecological systems underlying them, awe extends from trees and scenery to the little guys: insects, pollinators, fungi, microbes, and the invisible cycles that balance each system. A child may understand the intricacy of nature by staring at a cluster of ants for twenty minutes, awed by their bodily strength and assembly-line teamwork. That's why it's so important to grant young kids the opportunity to learn outdoors and to push for inclusivity and equity in those opportunities. The accessibility of awe is something to consider—especially for folks who live in urban areas and are unable to easily travel into nature or be awed by a starry sky outside their window.

Finally, you can find universal awe in green technology. Green Tech exhibitions, such as those I recall from the U.S. Science and Engineering Festival, never fail to attract crowds of all ages. From high-efficiency nanoparticles such as *graphene* (one atom thick but stronger than steel and lighter than paper!), to ocean plastic-cleaning bots, to sleek electric vehicles like the Tesla Model S P100D, green innovations continue to defy the assumption that a sustainable future is "impossible" or "unrealistic." Friends of mine on the Duke Electric Vehicles Team designed a hydrogen fuel cell car and famously broke the Guinness World Record for fuel efficiency.[147] Duke buzzed with school spirit that came from awe and respect of their hard work. Sometimes the awe factor is what spurs open-mindedness toward a future of climate action.

---

147 "Duke Electric Vehicles," website homepage.

A SENSE OF PRIDE

It is fitting to start with the rolling landscapes of the United States—the "spacious skies," "purple mountains," and "amber waves of grain" we take for granted…. What would you give to keep those skies free of greenhouse gases, urban smog, and hazardous particulate matter…or to keep the amber waves alive rather than watch them succumb to drought? A sense of pride, and often patriotism, can propel guardianship.

The national parks of the United States are considered some of the most magnificent places in the world, drawing in upwards of 330 million visitors from around the world annually.[148] We take pride in them, as well as the animals that inhabit them, having restored the wolves in Yellowstone and passed effective policies to save bald eagles, our own national symbol, from near extinction.

Clean energy is another potential area for national pride. It's not just a question of energy independence (pride in U.S. autonomy) but a question of *who will be the world leaders in renewable energy technologies*? Older generations know what it's like to vie for technological leadership—the Space Race of the 1960s culminated in the United States landing a man on the moon. The loftiness of that goal didn't stop the United States from achieving it, nor was the question of how much we were spending to make it happen an obstacle to the intense national pride that followed.

"The United States leads the world in…" is a very agreeable phrase for many Americans. Usually, we're most proud of our

---

148 "National Park Tourism in the U.S.—Statistics & Facts," Statista.

economic or technological leadership...so why don't we take as much of a stand for leadership in clean energy? Climate policies? A well-being economy?

There is nothing more patriotic than safeguarding the future.

A SENSE OF FEAR

Fear is another emotion everyone has in common, though it may also manifest as denial, anger, pragmatism, or dogmatism. Consider the Yale study mentioned earlier in this book on global warming's Six Americas: Alarmed, Concerned, Cautious, Disengaged, Doubtful, Dismissive. In a sense, these are all responses to fear.

The most universal fears are the fear of losing family members, faltering food or job security, or giving up freedoms.

STEMpathy means acknowledging everyone has these personal fears and attempting to feel them *collectively*, recognizing the people whose family safety, job security, and resource supplies are already jeopardized by climate change. As illustrated in Chapter 10, we must be prepared to openly discuss grief and loss.

The coronavirus pandemic challenged us to confront fear and loss on an unprecedented scale. People died by the thousands every day; families stayed quarantined indoors to protect vulnerable members. After scientists warned the public directly about the spread of the virus, people flooded to supermarkets to buy disinfectant wipes and hand sanitizer out of fear. Scientists have warned the American public about climate change, and the same people shrug. Maybe belief isn't the issue—it might be the extent of *fear*, a rather selfish question of *how directly will (or won't) this issue affect me personally?*

For STEMpathy, fear must transcend self-preservation. Let yourself fear for the families whose houses border wildfires; let yourself anger for the tribal communities whose sacred ground and waterways are defiled by construction and transform anger into constructive political action. Vote, make calls, sign petitions, and send letters.

Another lesson I learned from past activists in this book is this: Recognize that pit-of-your-stomach feeling when you *know* something is wrong or unjust. Elevate personal climate change stories that will help others experience it with you. Follow the example of the 2015 *Juliana v. United States* lawsuit, in which twenty-one youth plaintiffs sued the federal government for knowingly causing climate change.[149] From the quintessentially American standpoint of personal freedoms, someone else's negligence or "right to do nothing" infringes upon your right to clean air and your personal freedom to enjoy a healthy climate.

A SENSE OF HUMOR

"It's getting hot in here," reads one activist's protest sign, a magic-marker Earth doodled below the text. He stands shirtless on Independence Avenue as someone in a polar bear suit dances unskillfully next to him.

---

149 Juliana v. United States, No. 18-36082 (9th Cir. 2020).

What a humorously morbid way to draw attention to the climate crisis!

In truth, room for humor is necessary in the climate movement. Humor is universal and tends to dispel perceptions of "hard-assery" in even the most ardent dissenters.

For instance, one Extinction Rebellion poster humorously acknowledges: "Ok—We Admit We're Annoying." (And then below, in very small letters, "Just Not as Annoying as Drought.")[150] And when the activist I talked with in Chapter 2 explained that one of Extinction Rebellion's tactics is to walk across a crosswalk carrying banners at an extremely slow pace...one can't help but laugh at the mental image.

Environmental humor is everywhere. It's in meme culture (I audibly groaned at a windmill meme labeled "Renewable energy? I'm a big fan"). It's in people's lamentations about future supplies of wine and chocolate, among other products, being threatened by climate change. And it's in art and media—one famous statue depicts a meeting room of politicians *still* discussing climate change as water pools around their necks in a flooded room.[151] Dark but brilliant. And, in this sense, humor is important because it always pulls back the corner of the curtain to some larger truth.

---

150 Extinction Rebellion, Global Rebellion Poster, October 2019.

151 Isaac Cordal, *Waiting for Climate Change*, 2013, submerged sculpture installation, Nantes, France.

Finding unity in generational humor is more complicated—there is no secret formula to something as subjective as humor.

However, animals are a fantastic example of subjects that seldom fail to delight any age. The inexplicably funny or "cute" mannerisms of charismatic species (a monkey snapping selfies on a stolen camera, a family of elephants painting, an octopus shutting itself in a jar) remind us that we share a special bond with animals.

Now, for the larger truth piece. My hope is even the most whimsical viral videos will continue to foster a universal protectiveness of animals among Americans...and we will find ways to connect their humorous "cuteness" to the alarming disclaimer that they are vulnerable to climate change. I'd also hope to extend that protectiveness beyond the most charismatic or "cute" human-like species and toward *all* vulnerable life forms, particularly plants (mangroves matter—there is nothing "cute" about eroding coastlines and mass flooding!) as well as lesser-known animals found in the United States. It circles back to the sense-of-pride argument.

A SENSE OF BELONGING

Finally, it helps to empathize with the fact that everyone craves a sense of belonging. This could mean a sense of physical belonging or place, as discussed in Chapter 8, as well as an ideological sense of belonging—the feeling that one's identity is understood and validated.

Notice how valuable it is to form action groups: the Raging Grannies for elderly women, RepublicEn for the Eco-Right, the Sunrise Movement for students, the American Farmland Trust project for concerned farmers, and the list goes on. Climate change is not a matter of rallying behind only old/young or only Democrat/Republican divides. There is room for absolutely everyone to belong in the climate movement. All we need is *concern* in common.

It also helps for all ages of environmentalists to have a sense of belonging in the workplace. Every generation has something to offer: Older generations have experience, high-level managerial or board positions, and the wisdom to teach; younger generations have fresh ideas, optimism, social media prowess, and passion. (And these are generalizations—older and younger generations often have the trait of passion in common.) Recognizing the unique talents of both, there is room to work together.

Older environmentalists—hire an intern!

Younger environmentalists—shadow a mentor!

Teenage activist Alexandria Villaseñor also calls for collaboration between youth activists and experienced scientists "so that the two can share in one another's respective knowledge and stubborn voices," a great way to further promote a sense of belonging.[152]

---

152 Kitty Pollack and Anna Giorgi, "The Climate Movement Is Open for Business," The Aspen Institute, April 20, 2020.

According to Thomas Friedman, the future isn't so much about what we know. It's about what we can *do* with what we know.

We have the climate science—to fill in the policy gaps will require us to keep forming alliances and coalitions based upon shared experiences of awe, pride, fear, humor, and belonging.

THE CONVICTION TO LISTEN

Several years ago, I was on a hike in the northeast with a few of my closest childhood friends. These were friends I only got to see periodically in the summertime, so we always tried to make the most of it by swimming in the river, racing up mountains, exploring the woods, and talking about anything and everything. This year, at age seventeen, we reached the topic of climate change.

I think it started when one of us, racing downhill in a rush of fitness adrenaline, stumbled over a rocky outcropping, lurched forward, and nearly flew down the mountainside, grabbing a tree branch just in the nick of time before becoming well acquainted with the laws of gravity. We all gasped. Then someone laughed.

"Whoa, man, you almost, like, died!"

More laughter.

My friend Robin*[153] chimed in, "Well, technically, aren't we all going to die one day? From a natural disaster or something? When climate change fucks us all?" (His choice of words were the least of the expletives we'd heard that afternoon.)

James,*[154] removing his camera from his backpack, shrugged and smiled.

"I don't know; man...climate change is not a thing."

James was from a typically conservative region of the U.S., and it had always been pretty clear his political background differed from mine. He was also one of the people I trusted most and respected greatly for his talent in the arts and photography. He was a friend around whom I could be wholly myself. Politics had never gotten in the way of our group's friendship—not because we avoided talking about the subject, but because we were too cynical and jaded a group of youth to let it get in the way at all; it was something we had always spoken about with some degree of detachment. Until today.

James fiddled with his camera. We walked in silence for a minute, twigs and leaves crunching under our sneakers. I could see everyone's pondering faces outlined in orange glow as dusk began to fall over the mountainside.

My twin brother spoke up. "Bro, climate change is happening already. Places are going underwater due to extreme weather

---

153 Names have been changed.

154 Names have been changed.

events and sea level rise. Our hurricanes have been insane. Stuff is changing."

"And there's a ton of data backing it," I chimed in.

It sounded odd to preface such heavy and profound topics of conversation with "bro," "dude," and "man."

James clarified his standpoint slightly. "What I mean to say is that the climate is changing, a lot, and it's getting so bad we've got to start doing things to fix it. It's natural fluxes we're talking about here; humans are not what is causing it. But that doesn't mean we shouldn't do anything about it."

That was something. It was actually hard to believe we shared the belief that climate action needs to be taken.

Yet at the time, I also asked myself whether I should go off on him on the "natural fluxes" piece. I envisioned myself arguing for human causation using the famous "hockey-stick" graph, showing a dramatic, unprecedented spike in global CO_2 concentration, which correlates perfectly with the Industrial Revolution. I compiled a mental list of the hottest-days-on-average graphs I would cite, the rudimentary ozone effect diagrams I would describe from second grade, and all the other data I would present him, whipping out my phone for visuals, spit flying from my mouth as I delivered my impassioned and imaginary speech.

Instead, I said nothing. I was thinking, processing, listening—somewhere between being non-confrontational and being paralyzed. Crunching over leaves on the mountainside,

I learned the hidden blessing of this conversational paralysis. Sometimes, nothing is the best thing to say.

The silence allowed James to continue his thought process. "The solution, I think, will be technology." Several friends murmured in agreement.

"Oh, okay, gotcha," I said, still biting my tongue. "Well, what do you think we should do?"

James spoke about self-driving electric cars. He spoke about artificial intelligence and computer programs, and I saw his eyes lighting up with each topic. I saw his passion for new and daring ideas, for the same sort of business creativity I see in his film productions. Before long, we were pondering everything from Space X to nanotechnology to geoengineering, evaluating the complex and sometimes mystifying nature of each development. I found myself nodding at what he was saying, no longer out of courtesy, but out of total agreement.

Despite our differing views on whether climate change was human-caused, I realized neither one of us thought climate change was a total hoax (regardless of what President Trump had attempted to circulate on Twitter). Furthermore, we had found common ground in our fascination with emerging technological solutions. What felt the most important in our conversation was that even the smallest acknowledgement of climate disruption *felt validating*. I decided we could delve into the human-causation data some other time.

Dusk began to fall as we picked our way down the last leg of the mountainside with caution, crickets chirping around us in the chorus of deep summer. We used a fallen log to cross over one final ditch while James and I wrapped up our conversation on the far-fetched brilliance of Elon Musk and Tesla Motors. Our conversation did eventually circle back to natural disasters.

"Who knows whether it'll be an earthquake, drought, or that overdue volcanic eruption under Yellowstone that hoses us anyway," James says.

"All I can say is, we gotta do something about climate change… or…*Elon Musk* may end up bailing us out of the apocalypse as a whole," he quipped.

I laughed alongside him.

"Badass."

"Total badass."

* * *

That hike taught me a difficult lesson to learn in environmental communication. In the very first moments of a conversation, it is more important for *people to feel listened to* than for you to feel like you've successfully argued the "rightness" of your perspective onto them.

Consider refraining from instantly launching into a reflexive environmental tirade, as tempting as it may be. The right time will arise for you to boldly defend the Earth. If you have a true relationship with someone, you will have many chances to do so. But there is only one shot to gain someone's trust and find real common ground with them through STEMpathy. Climate justice isn't always a speech to preach.

It's a conversation.

It's a good impression.

It's a hike in the woods that ends in laughter instead of bickering.

And sometimes, it's a planted seed that grows, day by day, to ultimately change someone's mind.

CHAPTER 14

BE A STORYTELLER

Only when we have the courage to tell the truth about our old stories will the new stories arrive to guide us. Stories that recognize that the natural world and all its inhabitants have limits. Stories that teach us how to care for each other and regenerate life within those limits. Stories that put an end to the myth of endlessness once and for all.

—NAOMI KLEIN

THE TED MODEL OF STORYTELLING

Why are we so addicted to TED Talks?

Is it a rush of adrenaline, watching the speaker command the stage undaunted by their audience?

Is it a secret sense of smugness, feeling ever-so-slightly smarter after being enlightened on a nuanced topic?

Or is it simply the empathy that comes with giving another human your undivided attention for five sacred minutes?

TED Talks, delivered and enjoyed by curious people of all ages, are one of the twenty-first century's biggest treasures in terms of climate communication and making science more accessible to everyone. During any great Talk, the room sometimes erupts in laughter and sometimes sits in stunned silence, and each presentation seems to take on its own personality as speakers respond differently to an abstract prompt.

In theory, someone could gather a whole crowd of people into a room to explain to them, fact by fact, why climate change is dangerous. But without any sort of hook or emotional narrative, how likely is it that the room will a) listen or b) actually retain that information? Like any captivating TED Talk, your case on climate change should be structured as a narrative with a beginning, middle, and end. The audience is drawn into the shoes of the speaker and empathizes with them.

Some people hate on TED Talks for being too formulaic. Pace back and forth. Shoot a rhetorical question to the audience. Intellectual pause. Clasp hands together climactically. But, as I see it, scientific data presentations are equally formulaic. Introduction. Propose hypothesis. Explain methods. Results. Point to figures. Conclusion. While both are beautiful forms of communication, which would you rather listen to if you wanted to truly understand the quirks, worldviews, and idiosyncrasies of your human presenter?

And you don't have to give a literal TED Talk onstage to share your compelling stories. It could be an elevator pitch, a conversation at a party, a congressional testimony, a speech, or a presentation.

Anyone who has given a presentation is probably familiar with what I would call the Speaker's Dilemma: balancing factuality and the obligation to bolster a presentation with facts and figures with the need to feel interesting.

One of my friends opened his speech to a room full of young scientists with "Each and every one of you in this room is lazy." And I think he's right. Even as budding scientists, we are constrained by two factors that make us very human: a dwindling attention span and a love of imagery-fueled storytelling. Yet I've learned it is a nervous scientist's instinct to retreat into technicalities, to vomit out five minutes of research jargon. Fighting this urge, we strive for the magical feeling of captivating our audience onstage, suspended somewhere between encyclopedia and entertainer.

What makes a great TED Talk—or any speed-pitch conversation, really—is achieving an elusive harmony between facts and narrative.

THE ART AND ETHICS OF CLIMATE STORYTELLING

People will offer you different strategies on climate storytelling, but I compiled a list of five big ones based on my conversations with old and young activists:

- **Find that harmony between facts and narrative**: As expressed in Chapter 12, it matters to do your research and know your facts! Fuse them with personal stories (see ethical guideline prompt) and look for patterns in your facts that you can balance with a narrative. If you paint any characters as villains, heroes, or victims, are you doing so mindfully without oversimplifying the facts of the story?

- **Follow ethical guidelines**: There are ways to tell a compelling climate story without exploiting other people's experiences. If you're telling or writing someone else's story, ask yourself if there's any way that person could be telling it instead of you. Is there a way to create space for that? Otherwise, obtain their full consent and oversight in how you facilitate sharing their story. (This is especially important for white people telling stories of people of color, able-bodied people telling stories of people with disabilities, etc.)[155] Ask yourself, who might this story benefit by telling it?

- **Language matters**: Be intentional in your word choice; language is what often drives us apart. For example, it's amazing how much better a "carbon fee," or a "carbon price," goes over compared to a "carbon tax." Another example I find particularly funny is when Bob Shamansky, a Democrat from Ohio, complained about nicknaming the warming phenomenon the "greenhouse effect" because he'd always loved visiting greenhouses. He proposed we call it the "microwave oven" effect, because unlike a lush cottage of blossoming plants, "we are

---

155 Abesha Shiferaw, "How to Tell Compelling Stories While Avoiding Exploitation," *Nonprofit Technology Conference*, August 13, 2018.

getting cooked."[156] A little too late to heed his warning but an illustrative point on language, nonetheless.

- **Follow the three "Ps" checklist**: I don't take credit for this one. MIT Professor Susan Solomon devised the three "Ps" of whether people will take action to successfully address an environmental issue: *Is it **Perceptible**? Is it **Personal**? Are the solutions understood to be **Practical**?*[157] Consider ozone depletion and the ozone hole—though invisible like global warming, the "ozone hole" imagery made people see the problem (perceptible). Plus, the dangers of radiation affect everyone (personal). And finally, cheaper alternatives to CFC aerosol sprays existed (practical).

- **Focus on the Visible**: Sometimes, stories speak for themselves. In Venice, for example, the Council Chambers flooded with water only a few moments after the council voted down climate change measures.[158] In Standing Rock, artist Cannupa Hanska Luger crafted mirror-shields for water protectors to hold so police would look at the protest formation and see themselves.[159] Visuals are powerful. Cameron Oglesby, a colleague of mine, created the

---

156 Nathaniel Rich, "Losing Earth: The Decade We Almost Stopped Climate Change," *The New York Times*, August 1, 2018.

157 Helen Hill, "A Brief History of Environmental Successes," *MIT News*, November 9, 2017.

158 Eric Mack, "Venice Council Chambers Flood After Officials Vote Down Climate Change Measures," *Forbes*, November 14, 2019.

159 Cannupa Hanska Luger, "Mni Wiconi: Mirror Shield Project," gallery website.

Enviro-Art Gallery to further explore visual storytelling for that very reason.[160]

∗ ∗ ∗

FINDING YOUR ELEVATOR PITCH

If you had five minutes, how would you answer the question *why does climate change matter to you?*

It's not an easy question.

A good place to start is by researching climate facts for your hometown or place of residence. Consider your personal identities and how climate change will affect each of them. Tell the story of why *you* care; concisely answer the "so what?" question. You might have an answer in common with other storytellers.

Reflect on…

Chapters 4-5: What do you want for your kids?
Chapter 6: What are you willing to negotiate?
Chapter 7: What moves your spirit?
Chapter 8: What places matter to you?
Chapter 9: What makes you sing?
Chapter 10: What makes you grieve?

And if you have an answer that is concise, compelling, and above all, sincere, there will be no reason to dismiss you.

---

160 "The Enviro-Art Gallery," Rubenstein Arts Center.

SHOWING UP IN THE GRASSROOTS

Finally, whether you have a story of your own to share or not, the key to being able to call yourself an activist is *showing up.*

Defy the "Issue-Attention cycle" mentioned in Chapter 1. Break away from performative activism and establish a routine of commitment.

- Write letters to political leaders encouraging climate action. (Don't hold back—Mari Copeny, a.k.a. water and racial justice activist "Little Miss Flint," started her career by writing a letter to President Obama when she was eight.)
- Make calls if you're a fan of phone banking.
- Short on time? Donate money. Support local climate and environmental justice NGOs in your community.
- Circulate petitions and event flyers on social media.
- Attend rallies, hearings, or educational events.
- Drive carpools to allow others to show up (My graduate colleague Kat Horvath spends her time doing this—she is hugely helpful to young folks who can't drive yet.)
- Look for political depolarization workshops or intergenerational dialogue classes in your area. Learn "intergenerational reparative justice" together, which means *learning to forgive.*[161]
- Commit to learning more about the environment.
- Enrich the list of thought leaders you follow.
- Spark conversation.
- Vote.

---

161 Ben Almassi, "Climate Change and the Need for Intergenerational Reparative Justice," *Journal of Agricultural and Environmental Ethics* 30, (2017): 199–212

As *Growing Up in The Grassroots* draws to an end, your climate story begins.

Your ongoing narrative will depend on the roles you choose: passive supporter or warrior? Bully or ally? Free-rider or activist?

"We have no choice but to succeed," Francis Grant-Suttie commented. The "we" doesn't just rest on Generation Greta—it rests on everyone.

"I don't think our generation won the war, but we moved the needle," he reflected. "We put it on the map...you guys are gonna finish it off."

"But you won't be alone, as those of us who went before will not be cheering from the sidelines but *alongside you.* We sit on boards now, have vast networks of like-minded citizens, have extra cash from our lifelong labors, and spend our money supporting environmentalism and investing in green markets. It takes a global village."

Other activists expressed similar viewpoints: They *want to help us achieve justice.* They have faith in our climate fight. Day after day, their encouragement inspires.

And there are so many things I want to say in return...

"Okay, boomer" is not one of them.

I want to say, "Thank you, boomer."

I want to say *we're ready* to march, arm in arm, through the grassroots of a climate movement whose seeds have been carefully planted by older generations of activists.

Across generations, with the energy of youth and the wisdom of elders, we are growing the movement together.

AFTERTHOUGHTS

———

I'm putting the finishing touches on this book during one of the most difficult times my country has experienced.

The coronavirus pandemic continues to take lives and separate families. A sobering death toll will be announced on the evening news tonight. It will be hard to recover from this period of grief.

Accompanying that death toll is a surge of murders and violence against innocent, unarmed black people in the United States. Riots and protests in Minneapolis and beyond exemplify a necessary form of rebellion beyond the protests described in this book—reminding us there are times when dissent and disobedience *must boldly persist with whatever tactics are necessary.*

Amid unrest and lockdown, the Trump administration is attempting to halt the enforcement of clear air and clean water regulations for polluting companies.

The months leading up to the publication of *Growing Up in the Grassroots* have been nothing short of a challenge.

And it has been difficult crafting a message of hope and optimism when it seems that every day a news story undermines that unifying thesis.

But we *must* continue to search for unity.

In many ways, the pandemic is an intergenerational truce. Young people isolate themselves in quarantine for the sake of protecting older people in the same way older people fight to keep this planet as livable as possible for younger people. Much like the damages of climate change, the most vulnerable demographics are infants, the elderly, and people with pre-existing conditions. We are living through an era that probably won't have a "back to normal."

I don't know how this book will be received in ten, twenty, or thirty years. There will most definitely be more environmental grievances to add to the Litany of Despair but also the very real possibility that the structural changes we've been fighting for in the grassroots will start happening.

I also want to recognize the timing of this book's publication falls only months before the 2020 presidential election, which, in either direction of its possible outcome, will be an election that changes history.

This book, then, will serve as a sort of time capsule into the reflections of activists living in Trump's America. The interviews I conducted *made* this book—these are the people who strengthen the grassroots when everything else is uprooted; these are the voices whose passion and bold outcry will give the "Roaring 2020s" a new meaning.

Wangari Maathai, a Kenyan activist and Nobel Peace Prize winner, offers a fragment of wisdom that keeps me resilient in that work:

"The little grassroots people can change this world."

Live by those words, and keep fighting. I'll see you in the grassroots.

APPENDIX

Introduction

Cook, John, Naomi Oreskes, Peter T. Doran, William R. L. Anderegg, Bart Verheggen, Ed W. Maibach, J. Stuart Carlton, Stephan Lewandowsky, Andrew G. Skuce, Sarah A. Green, Dana Nuccitelli, Peter Jacobs, Mark Richardson, Bärbel Winkler, Rob Painting, and Ken Rice. "Consensus on Consensus: A Synthesis of Consensus Estimate on Human-Caused Global Warming." *Environmental Research Letters* 11, no. 4 (April 2016). DOI:10.1088/1748-9326/11/4/048002

Dictionary.com, Slang ed. s.v. "OK, boomer." Accessed December 29, 2019. https://www.dictionary.com/e/slang/ok-boomer/

Gibbens, Sarah. "The Amazon Is Burning at Record Rates—and Deforestation Is to Blame." *National Geographic*. August 21, 2019. https://www.nationalgeographic.com/environment/2019/08/wildfires-in-amazon-caused-by-deforestation/#-close

Intergovernmental Panel on Climate Change, 2018: Special Report on Global Warming of 1.5°C. IPCC, 2018. https://www.ipcc.ch/sr15/chapter/spm/

Intergovernmental Panel on Climate Change, 2018: Summary for Policymakers. In: *Special Report on Global Warming of 1.5°C.*

IPCC, 2018. https://www.ipcc.ch/2018/10/08/summary-for-policymakers-of-ipcc-special-report-on-global-warming-of-1-5c-approved-by-governments/

James, Lauren E. "Half of the Great Barrier Reef Is Dead." *National Geographic,* August 2018. https://www.nationalgeographic.com/magazine/2018/08/explore-atlas-great-barrier-reef-coral-bleaching-map-climate-change/

Lenton, Timothy M., Johan Rockström, Owen Gaffney, Stefan Rahmstorf, Katherine Richardson, Will Steffen, and Hans Joachim Schellnhuber. "Climate Tipping Points—Too Risky to Bet Against." *Nature* 575, no. 7784 (November 2019): 592–95. https://www.nature.com/articles/d41586-019-03595-0

Lindsey, Rebecca. "Climate Change: Atmospheric Carbon Dioxide." NOAA Climate.gov. February 20, 2020. https://www.climate.gov/news-features/understanding-climate/climate-change-atmospheric-carbon-dioxide

Lorenz, Taylor. "'OK Boomer' Marks the End of Friendly Generational Relations." *The New York Times,* October 29, 2019. https://www.nytimes.com/2019/10/29/style/ok-boomer.html

Mediakix. "20 TikTok Stats for Marketers: TikTok Demographics, Statistics, & Key Data." Accessed December 20, 2019. https://mediakix.com/blog/top-tik-tok-statistics-demographics/

National Aeronautics and Space Administration. "Arctic Sea Ice Minimum." Jet Propulsion Laboratory. Accessed April 10, 2020. https://climate.nasa.gov/vital-signs/arctic-sea-ice/

National Oceanic and Atmospheric Administration. "What is a ghost forest?" National Ocean Service website. Last modified April 9, 2020. https://oceanservice.noaa.gov/facts/ghost-forest.html

Reinhart, RJ. "Global Warming Age Gap: Younger Americans Most Worried." Gallup Poll News Release. May 11, 2018. https://

news.gallup.com/poll/234314/global-warming-age-gap-younger-americans-worried.aspx

Smith, Adam B. "2017 U.S. Billion-Dollar Weather and Climate Disasters: A Historic Year in Context." NOAA Beyond the Data. January 8, 2018. https://www.climate.gov/news-features/blogs/beyond-data/2017-us-billion-dollar-weather-and-climate-disasters-historic-year

Tedesco, M., T. Moon, J. K. Andersen, J. E. Box, J. Cappelen, R. S. Fausto, X. Fettweis, B. Loomis, K. D. Mankoff, T. Mote, C. J. P. P. Smeets, D. van As, and R. S. W. van de Wal. "Greenland Ice Sheet." In *Arctic Report Card: Update for 2019* (NOAA Arctic Program, 2019). Accessed January 2, 2020. https://arctic.noaa.gov/Report-Card/Report-Card-2019/ArtMID/7916/ArticleID/842/Greenland-Ice-Sheet

United Nations. "Climate Action Summit 2019—Morning Session." September 23, 2019. Video, 41:00. https://youtu.be/haewHZ8ubKA?t=2460

Chapter 1

Anthony Downs, "Up and Down with Ecology—The 'Issue-Attention Cycle,'" *National Affairs,* no. 43 (2020, original 1972): 39-50. https://www.nationalaffairs.com/public_interest/detail/up-and-down-with-ecologythe-issue-attention-cycle

Ballew, Matthew, Jennifer Marlon, Seth Rosenthal, Abel Gustafson, John Kotcher, Edward Maibach, and Anthony Leiserowitz. "Do Younger Generations Care More about Global Warming?" *Yale Program on Climate Change Communication.* June 11, 2019. https://climatecommunication.yale.edu/publications/do-younger-generations-care-more-about-global-warming/

Kitchell, Mark. *A Fierce Green Fire: The Battle for a Living Planet* (First Run Features and Bullfrog Films, 2012). From Sundance Film Festival 2012. https://www.afiercegreenfire.com/

Kline, Benjamin. *First Along the River: A Brief History of the U.S. Environmental Movement,* 4th ed. Lanham: Rowman & Littlefield Publishers, 2011. https://books.google.com/books?id=F9ZSxXSeq2MC

Perez, Monica and Binkley, Brad. "DNB: Millions of Children Coerced into Climate Strike Protest by Bad Parents." September 9, 2019. *The Propaganda Report.* Podcast, Spotify, 24:44. https://open.spotify.com/show/1SfS3kDDYOTeYDZ2UD-V6wQ?si=m7mY9OqsRGim4VEX78sM4g

Rich, Nathaniel. "Losing Earth: The Decade We Almost Stopped Climate Change." *The New York Times.* August 1, 2018. https://www.nytimes.com/interactive/2018/08/01/magazine/climate-change-losing-earth.html

Chapter 2

BBC News. "What is Extinction Rebellion and What Does it Want?" October 7, 2019. https://www.bbc.com/news/uk-48607989

"Extinction Rebellion." Website homepage. Accessed Dec 17, 2019. https://rebellion.earth/

Rosane, Olivia. "'I'm Putting My Life on Hold': 22 Climate Activists Arrested." *EcoWatch.* November 13, 2018. https://www.ecowatch.com/22-climate-activists-arrested-london-2619516359.html

Chapter 3

"Introduction: The Earth Day Story and Gaylord Nelson." Nelson Institute for Environmental Studies. Accessed March 30, 2020. http://nelsonearthday.net/earth-day/

Lelyveld, Joseph. "Mood is Joyful as City Gives Its Support." *The New York Times* Digital Archives. April 23, 1970. https://www.nytimes.com/1970/04/23/archives/mood-is-joyful-as-city-gives-its-support-millions-join-earth-day.html

Lemann, Nicholas. "When the Earth Moved: What Happened to the Environmental Movement?" *The New Yorker.* April 8, 2013. https://www.newyorker.com/magazine/2013/04/15/when-the-earth-moved?currentPage=all

Mai-Duc, Christine. "The 1969 Santa Barbara Oil Spill that Changed Oil and Gas Exploration Forever." *Los Angeles Times.* May 20, 2015. https://www.latimes.com/local/lanow/la-me-ln-santa-barbara-oil-spill-1969-20150520-htmlstory.html

"New Zealand lawmaker shuts down heckler: 'OK, boomer." *CNN.* November 17, 2019. Video, 0:14. https://youtu.be/ipe9WxUf-h7w?t=14

RepublicEn.org. Energy and Enterprise Initiative. Accessed April 2, 2020. https://www.republicen.org/

Rich, Nathaniel. "Losing Earth: The Decade We Almost Stopped Climate Change." *The New York Times.* August 1, 2018. https://www.nytimes.com/interactive/2018/08/01/magazine/climate-change-losing-earth.html

Yoder, Kate. "On Climate Change, Younger Republicans Now Sound Like Democrats." *Grist.* September 9, 2019. https://grist.org/article/on-climate-change-younger-republicans-now-sound-like-democrats/

Chapter 4

Buttigieg, Karen and Pace, Paul. "Positive Youth Action Towards Climate Change." *Journal of Teacher Education for Sustainability* 15, no. 1 (June 1, 2013): 15–47. https://doi.org/10.2478/jtes-2013-0002

"Indigenous Teenager to Advocate for Clean Water in Canada at United Nations Forum." CFWE Radio. September 26, 2019. http://www.cfweradio.ca/news/alberta-news/indigenous-teenager-to-advocate-for-clean-water-in-canada-at-united-nations-forum/

Kamenetz, Anya. "Most Teachers Don't Teach Climate Change; 4 In 5 Parents Wish They Did." April 22, 2019. In *NPR Morning Edition*, radio show. https://www.npr.org/2019/04/22/714262267/most-teachers-dont-teach-climate-change-4-in-5-parents-wish-they-did

Martinez, Xiuhtezcatl (@xiuhtezcatl). "Raise our youth with the compassion to protect our elders." Instagram. March 14, 2020.

"Meet Autumn Peltier, Teen Water Warrior." CBC Podcasts. Last modified August 6, 2019. https://www.cbc.ca/radio/secretlifeofcanada/meet-autumn-peltier-teen-water-warrior-1.5237845

Wilson, Carla. "Effective Approaches to Connect Children with Nature." Department of Conservation Te Papa Atawbai (July 2011): 7. https://www.doc.govt.nz/Documents/getting-involved/students-and-teachers/effective-approaches-to-connect-children-with-nature.pdf

Chapter 5

Bacon, John. "No Future, No Children: Teens Refusing to Have Kids Until There's Action on Climate Change." *USA Today*. September 29, 2019. https://www.usatoday.com/story/news/nation/2019/09/19/no-future-no-children-pledge-teens-refuse-have-kids-until-climate-change-action/2372010001/

Diamond, Emily P. "The Influence of Identity Salience on Framing Effectiveness: An Experiment." (In press, 2020). *Political Psychology*. doi: 10.1111/pops.12669

"How Parenthood Affects Climate Change Skeptics." *Ways and Means Podcast* (transcript). Sanford School of Public Policy. September 2020. https://waysandmeansshow.org/

Leiserowitz, Anthony, Edward Maibach, Connie Roser-Renouf, Seth Rosenthal, Matthew Cutler, and John Kotcher. "Climate Change in the American Mind: March 2018." *Yale Program on Climate Change Communication*. April 17, 2018. https://cli-

matecommunication.yale.edu/publications/climate-change-
american-mind-march-2018/

Matthews, Mark K., Nick Bowlin, and Benjamin Hulac. "Inside the
Sunrise Movement (It Didn't Happen by Accident)." *E&E News.*
December 3, 2018. https://www.eenews.net/stories/1060108439

Scher, Avichai. "'Climate Grief': The Growing Emotional Toll of
Climate Change." *NBC News.* December 14, 2018. https://www.
nbcnews.com/health/mental-health/climate-grief-growing-
emotional-toll-climate-change-n946751

Chapter 6

Anders, William. *Earthrise.* 1968. Photograph. NASA website.
https://www.nasa.gov/multimedia/imagegallery/image_fea-
ture_1249.html

Ballew, Matthew, Jennifer Marlon, Seth Rosenthal, Abel Gustafson,
John Kotcher, Edward Maibach, and Anthony Leiserowitz.
"Do Younger Generations Care More about Global Warming?" *Yale Program on Climate Change Communication.* June
11, 2019 https://climatecommunication.yale.edu/publications/
do-younger-generations-care-more-about-global-warming/

Bonnie, Robert, Emily Pechar Diamond, and Elizabeth Rowe.
"Understanding Rural Attitudes Toward the Environment
and Conservation in America." *The Nicholas Institute for
Environmental Policy Solutions.* Report. March 2020. https://
nicholasinstitute.duke.edu/sites/default/files/publications/
understanding-rural-attitudes-toward-environment-conser-
vation-america.pdf

Campbell, Troy H., and Aaron C. Kay. "Solution aversion: On the
relation between ideology and motivated disbelief." *Journal
of Personality and Social Psychology 107. no. 5 (2014)*: 809–824.
https://doi.org/10.1037/a0037963

Diamond, Emily, Robert Bonnie, and Elizabeth Rowe. "Rural Attitudes on Climate Change: Lessons from National and Midwest Polling and Focus Groups." Report (in press). 2020.

Hardin, Garrett. "Limits to Growth—Two Views: We Live on a Spaceship." *Bulletin of the Atomic Scientists* 28, no. 9 (November 1972): 23-24. Google Books.

Hawken, Paul, Amory Lovins, and L. Hunter Lovins. *Natural Capitalism: Creating the Next Industrial Revolution*. Boston: Little, Brown, and Co., 1999.

Henderson, Caroline A. "Letters from the Dust Bowl." *The Atlantic*. May 1936. https://www.theatlantic.com/magazine/archive/1936/05/letters-from-the-dust-bowl/308897/

Landon-Lane, John, Hugh Rockoff, and Richard Steckel. "Droughts, Floods, and Financial Distress in the United States." *NBER Working Paper No. 15596* (December 2009). doi:10.3386/w15596.

Lebow, Victor. "Price Competition in 1955." *Journal of Retailing* 31, no. 1 (Spring 1955): 5-10. http://ablemesh.co.uk/PDFs/journal-of-retailing1955.pdf

Nash, Roderick Frazier, ed. *American Environmentalism: Readings in Conservation History, Third Edition*. McGraw-Hill, 1990.

NPR Soundbite (2000), In "Earth Day Founder Gaylord Nelson Dies," *NPR Morning Edition*. Radio show. July 4, 2005. https://www.npr.org/templates/story/story.php?storyId=4728532

Romm, Joseph. "The Next Dust Bowl." *Nature* 478 (October 2011): 450-451. https://doi.org/10.1038/478450a

Roth, Adam. "Sustainability: The Launch of Spaceship Earth." *Nature* 527 (November 2015): 443-445. https://doi.org/10.1038/527443a

Stahel, Walter R. "The Circular Economy." *Nature* 531, no. 7595 (March 2016): 435-438. https://www.nature.com/news/polopoly_fs/1.19594!/menu/main/topColumns/topLeftColumn/pdf/531435a.pdf

Phillips, Leigh. "The Degrowth Delusion." *openDemocracy*. Last modified August 30, 2019. https://www.opendemocracy.net/en/oureconomy/degrowth-delusion/

Purdy, Jedediah. *After Nature: A Politics for the Anthropocene.* Cambridge: Harvard University Press, 2015.

Shreiber, Melody. "The Coronavirus and the Limits of Individual Climate Action." *The New Republic.* Last modified April 27, 2020. https://newrepublic.com/article/157450/coronavirus-limits-individual-climate-action

USDA. "Food Waste FAQs" Accessed May 2, 2020. https://usda.gov/foodwaste.faqs

Wiener, Jonathan B. "The Tragedy of the Uncommons: On the Politics of Apocalypse." *Global Policy* 7, supp. no. 1 (May 2016): 67.-80. https://doi.org/10.1111/1758-5899.12319

Worster, Donald. *Dust Bowl: The Southern Plains in the 1930s.* Oxford: Oxford University Press, 2004. Google Books. https://books.google.com/books/about/Dust_Bowl.html?id=8fM-ZWXPe_QC

Chapter 7

"Atheism Doubles Among Gen Z." Barna Group. January 24, 2018. https://www.barna.com/research/atheism-doubles-among-generation-z/

Berry, Wendell. *Recollected Essays, 1965-1980.* In Nash, Roderick Frazier, ed. *American Environmentalism: Readings in Conservation History, Third Edition.* McGraw-Hill, 1990.

Coward, Harold. "Hindu Views of Nature and the Environment." 2003. In: Selin, Helaine (eds). *Nature Across Cultures: Views of Nature and the Environment in Non-Western Cultures,* vol. 4. 411-419. https://doi.org/10.1007/978-94-017-0149-5_21

Goldberg, Matthew H., Abel Gustafson, Matthew Ballew, Seth Rosenthal, and Anthony Leiserowitz. "Engaging Christians in the Issue of Climate Change." *Yale Program on Climate Change Communication*. July 12, 2019. https://climatecommunication. yale.edu/publications/engaging-christians-in-the-issue-of-climate-change/

Leiserowitz, Anthony, Edward Maibach, Connie Roser-Renouf, Seth Rosenthal, Matthew Cutler, and John Kotcher. "Climate Change in the American Mind: March 2018." *Yale Program on Climate Change Communication*. April 17, 2018. https://climatecommunication.yale.edu/publications/climate-change-american-mind-march-2018/

New Oxford American Dictionary (digital), American English ed. s.v. "steward." Accessed March 28, 2020 through macOS High Sierra Dictionary Version 2.2.2 (203).

Nick O. "Borat Goes to Church Part 1." April 16, 2020. Video. https://www.youtube.com/watch?v=R8lAIfTwHuw

Odeh Al-Jayyousi, "How Islam Can Represent a Model for Environmental Stewardship." UN Environment Programme. June 21, 2018. https://www.unenvironment.org/news-and-stories/story/how-islam-can-represent-model-environmental-stewardship

Purdy, Jedediah. *After Nature: A Politics for the Anthropocene*. Cambridge: Harvard University Press, 2015.

Santiago, José. "15 Quotes on Climate Change by World Leaders." World Economic Forum. November 27, 2015. https://www.weforum.org/agenda/2015/11/15-quotes-on-climate-change-by-world-leaders/

Van Houtan, Kyle S., and Stuart L. Pimm. "The Various Christian Ethics of Species Conservation." In *Religion and the New Ecology: Environmental Prudence in a World in Flux*. Notre Dame: University of Notre Dame Press, 2006. 116-147. http://people.duke.edu/~ksv2/articles/03_VanHoutan_Pimm_2006_various_christian_ethics.pdf

Chapter 9

Ecomusicology Review. "What is Ecomusicology?" Accessed April 24, 2020. https://ecomusicology.info/info/

Roy, Carole. "The Original Raging Grannies: Using Creative and Humorous Protests for Political Education." The Raging Grannies Herstory. Accessed February 26, 2020. https://raginggrannies.org/herstory/

The Raging Grannies. "Our Philosophy." Accessed February 26, 2020. https://raginggrannies.org/philosophy/

Stage Parades. "Jackson Browne—Before the Deluge (+ lyrics 1974)." August 3, 2012. Video. https://youtu.be/32KTKXZZ-BI.

Chapter 10

Atkinson, Jennifer. "My Students Aren't Snowflakes, They're Badasses." *The Denver Post.* June 1, 2018. https://www.denverpost.com/2018/06/01/my-students-arent-snowflakes-they-re-badasses/

Clayton, Susan, Christie Manning, Kirra Krygsman, and Meighen Speiser. "Mental Health and Our Changing Climate: Impacts, Implications, and Guidance." Washington, D.C.: American Psychological Association and ecoAmerica. 2017. https://www.apa.org/news/press/releases/2017/03/mental-health-climate.pdf

"Dictionary.com's Word of the Year for 2019 Is…" Dictionary.com. Accessed February 2, 2020. https://www.dictionary.com/e/word-of-the-year/

Dictionary.com, Pop Culture ed. s.v. "existential." Accessed February 2, 2020. https://www.dictionary.com/e/pop-culture/existential-crisis/

Lil Dicky. "Lil Dicky—Earth (Official Music Video)." April 19, 2019. Video. https://www.youtube.com/watch?v=pvuN_WvF1to

Peterson, Blake. "UW Bothell Seminar Aims to Help Students Cope with Climate Change Concerns." *Bothell-Kenmore*

Reporter. February 21, 2018. https://www.bothell-reporter.com/
life/uw-bothell-seminar-aims-to-help-students-cope-with-cli-
mate-change-concerns/

Rosa-Aquino, Paola. "The Life-Altering, World-Ending Topic
They're Still Not Teaching You About in School. *Grist.* June 4,
2019. https://grist.org/article/climate-change-education-col-
lege-graduation/

Chapter 11

Funk, Cary, and Kim Parker. "Racial Diversity and Discrimination
in the U.S. STEM Workforce." *Pew Research Center's Social
& Demographic Trends Project.* January 9, 2018. https://www.
pewsocialtrends.org/2018/01/09/blacks-in-stem-jobs-are-es-
pecially-concerned-about-diversity-and-discrimination-in-
the-workplace/.

Funk, Cary. "Mixed Messages about Public Trust in Science." *Issues
in Science and Technology.* Pew Research Center. December 8,
2017. https://www.pewresearch.org/science/2017/12/08/mixed-
messages-about-public-trust-in-science/

Goldberg, Matthew, Abel Gustafson, Seth Rosenthal, John Kotcher,
Edward Maibach, and Anthony Leiserowitz. "For the First
Time, the Alarmed Are Now the Largest of Global Warming's Six Americas." *Yale Program on Climate Change Communication,* 2020. https://climatecommunication.yale.edu/
publications/for-the-first-time-the-alarmed-are-now-the-
largest-of-global-warmings-six-americas/.

Leiserowitz, Anthony, Edward Maibach, and Connie Roser-Renouf.
"Global Warming's Six Americas." *Yale Program on Climate
Change Communication,* 2009-2020. https://climatecommuni-
cation.yale.edu/about/projects/global-warmings-six-americas/.

U.S. Congress. House. Energy Innovation and Carbon Dividend
Act of 2019. HR 763. 116th Cong., 1st sess. Introduced in House

January 24, 2019. https://www.congress.gov/bill/116th-congress/house-bill/763/text

Chapter 12

Barron, Laignee. "Here's What the EPA's Website Looks Like After a Year of Climate Change Censorship." *Time*. March 1, 2018.

Center for Research on Environmental Decisions. "The Psychology of Climate Change Communication." Accessed March 25, 2020. http://guide.cred.columbia.edu/guide/sec1.html

Cook, John, Dana Nuccitelli, Sarah A. Green, Mark Richardson, Bärbel Winkler, Rob Painting, Robert Way, Peter Jacobs, and Andrew Skuce. "Quantifying the Consensus on Anthropogenic Global Warming in the Scientific Literature." *Environmental Research Letters* 8, no. 2 (2013). https://doi.org/10.1088/1748-9326/8/2/024024.

Da, Jiawei, Yi Ge Zhang, Gen Li, Xianqiang Meng, and Junfeng Ji. "Low CO_2 Levels of the Entire Pleistocene Epoch." *Nature Communications* 10, no.1 (2009): 1–9. https://doi.org/10.1038/s41467-019-12357-5.

D'Amato, Gerrano, Carolina Vitale, Annamaria De Martino, Giovanni Viegi, Maurizia Lanza, Antonio Molino, Alessandro Sanduzzi, Alessandro Vatrella, Isabella Annesi-Maesano, and Maria D'Amato. "Effects on Asthma and Respiratory Allergy of Climate Change and Air Pollution." *Multidisciplinary Respiratory Medicine* 10, no. 1 (2015): 39.

Fischer, Douglas. "Climate Risks as Conclusive as Link Between Smoking and Lung Cancer." *Scientific American*. March 19, 2014. https://www.scientificamerican.com/article/climate-risks-as-conclusive-as-link-between-smoking-and-lung-cancer/

Hawken, Paul, ed. *Drawdown: The Most Comprehensive Plan Ever Proposed to Reverse Global Warming.* New York: Penguin Books, 2017.

Mock, Brentin. "Message from the EPA: It's about Protecting People, Not Polar Bears." *Grist.* September 23, 2013. https://grist.org/climate-energy/message-from-the-epa-its-about-protecting-people-not-polar-bears/.

Moran, Greta. "1,656 Pages Too Long? Climate Report Coauthor Katharine Hayhoe Has 3 Takeaways." *Grist.* November 27, 2018.

NASA Jet Propulsion Laboratory. "Global Climate Change: Vital Signs of the Planet." Accessed March 26, 2020. https://climate.nasa.gov/

Saloojee, Yussuf and Elif Dagli. "Tobacco Industry Tactics for Resisting Public Policy on Health." *Bulletin of the World Health Organization* 78 (July 2000): 902–10. https://doi.org/10.1590/S0042-96862000000700007.

Skeptical Science. "Skeptical Science: Getting Skeptical About Global Warming Skepticism." Accessed March 27, 2020. https://www.skepticalscience.com/

World Health Organization. "Climate Change and Health." Accessed March 5, 2020. https://www.who.int/news-room/fact-sheets/detail/climate-change-and-health

"Yale Program on Climate Change Communication." Accessed March 26, 2020. https://climatecommunication.yale.edu/

Chapter 13

Cordal, Isaac. *Waiting for Climate Change.* 2013. Submerged sculpture installation. Nantes, France.

"Duke Electric Vehicles." Accessed April 2, 2020. http://www.duke-ev.org/

Extinction Rebellion. Global Rebellion Poster. October 2019.

Fuglei, Monica. "STEMpathy: Thomas Friedman's Case for Humanity in STEM Education." Resilient Educator. Accessed January 27, 2020. https://resilienteducator.com/classroom-resources/stempathy-stem-education/

Juliana v. United States, No. 18-36082. 9th Cir. 2020.

Pollack, Kitty and Anna Giorgi. "The Climate Movement Is Open for Business." The Aspen Institute. April 20, 2020. https://www.aspeninstitute.org/blog-posts/climate-movement-open-business/

Statista. "National Park Tourism in the U.S.—Statistics & Facts." Accessed March 13, 2020. https://www.statista.com/topics/2393/national-park-tourism-in-the-us/

Chapter 14

Almassi, Ben. "Climate Change and the Need for Intergenerational Reparative Justice." *Journal of Agricultural and Environmental Ethics* 30, (2017): 199-212. https://doi.org/10.1007/s10806-017-9661-z

Hill, Helen. "A Brief History of Environmental Successes." *MIT News.* November 9, 2017. http://news.mit.edu/2017/mit-professor-susan-solomon-examines-history-environmental-successes-1109

Luger, Cannupa Hanska. "Mni Wiconi: Mirror Shield Project." Gallery website. Accessed December 29, 2019. http://www.cannupahanska.com/mniwiconi/

Mack, Eric. "Venice Council Chambers Flood After Officials Vote Down Climate Change Measures." *Forbes.* November 14, 2019. https://www.forbes.com/sites/ericmack/2019/11/14/venice-council-chambers-flood-after-officials-vote-down-climate-change-measures/#74a0269d324c

Rich, Nathaniel. "Losing Earth: The Decade We Almost Stopped Climate Change." *The New York Times.* August 1, 2018. https://

www.nytimes.com/interactive/2018/08/01/magazine/climate-change-losing-earth.html

Rubenstein Arts Center. "The Enviro-Art Gallery." Accessed November 14, 2019. https://artscenter.duke.edu/event/the-enviro-art-gallery/

Shiferaw, Abesha. "How to Tell Compelling Stories While Avoiding Exploitation." *Nonprofit Technology Conference.* August 13, 2018. https://www.nten.org/article/how-to-tell-compelling-stories-while-avoiding-exploitation/

ACKNOWLEDGEMENTS

I have always dreamed of telling stories.

As a child, they were hand-drawn comic books, then geekily-themed podcasts, then oral history projects…and now, I find myself uttering the most improbable reflection: "I wrote a book."

The journey of *Growing Up in the Grassroots* has been eye-opening, gratifying, and far from easy. I am infinitely thankful for the people who helped me through every late night of editing and every moment of self-doubt. From the early support of friends and family to the successful crowdfunding campaign that brought this book to life, it feels fitting that this book was made possible by the same potent force that underlies the climate movement. It was people driven.

First, I want to thank my family for being a constant, inspiring presence in my life. I will never forget the creative buzz in our household as I researched and drafted the early stages of this book. Mom and Dad—you both have shown me, through your compassion and tolerance, that the message of this book rings true. I love you always.

Thank you to Dr. Rebecca Vidra, my environmental studies professor and mentor throughout this process. Your insightful feedback on my manuscript, and involvement of your students along the way, evidence what an exceptional professor and role model you are.

I am also grateful for everyone I interviewed over the course of this book. Not only are your stories the foundation of *Growing Up in the Grassroots,* but our hours of meaningful conversation were by far the most moving and rewarding part of this entire journey. Thank you for your time, your energy, and your example.

Special thanks to Frederick County Councilmember Kai Hagen for your support and insights. You exemplify true mentorship and leadership in climate action.

Thank you to my editors at New Degree Press, Cass Lauer, Jennifer Candiotti, Emily Kim, and John Chancey, for your support and patience. I'd also like to thank Professor Eric Koester and Brian Bies for guiding me through this long-awaited dream and turning it into a reality.

Finally, I'd like to thank everyone who pre-ordered, donated, and helped spread the word about *Growing Up in the Grassroots* to help it gather amazing momentum. I am sincerely grateful for you.

Aaron Moore

Mariusz Derezinski-Choo

Tiarra Cruz

Anne Macdonell

Brian Harris*

Katherine Li

Justin P. Wright*

Josephine Monmaney

Scott Rhodes

Alex Haight*

Rosa Golchin

Julia Orlidge*

Amanda J. Waugh*

Megan Knauer

Clayton Delp

Liz Regan Kiingi

Sandra S. Mulcahy*

Jennifer Freedman

Mia Kim

Cordell Pugh

Susan and David Currie

Dave Brandt

Ryan Bergamini

Karen Kaufman

Michael Waitzkin*

Chip Arnold

Douglas McGuire

Jim Dooley

Melissa A. Simmermeyer

Phyllis Robinson*

Jay and Karlyne Reilly

Tara Day Barnhart

Alex Oesterling

Francis Grant-Suttie*

Kim O'Shaughnessy

Christina Chalmers

Joey Weiss

Krystle Koontz

William Ferriby

Megan Richards

Bobby Radecki

Corey Null

Meryl Goeke

Anna Morrison

Paul Ternes*

Ayesham Khan

Erica Langan

Margaret Overton

Daniel Ryan

Dave Allen

Grace Dessert

Alyssa Nelson

Michael Lee

Gordon Reeves

Catherine McMillan

David Hart

Ariel Teitel

Joshua Hames

Anne and David Simms*

Peter Armbruster

Jory Weintraub

Lisa Avendt

Charlotte Clark*

Danan Mbozi and Family

David E. Reeves

Roy Currie

Ellen Gordon

Mary Barnett

Kesra Hoffman

Bertrand Cote

Elinor S. Currie*

Tom Pinkin

Stacy Peterson

Doug Hart*

Kevin Kelliher

Melanie Galloway

Gretchen Hundertmark

Jill Reeves

Valerie Wittkamper

Ahmed Hussain

Philippe Izedian

Craig Currie

Ann Truss

Kai Hagen

Ritchie Porter

Matthew Helmbrecht

Holly Larisch*

Leo Akers

Rebecca Dean

Cheryl Lower

Lynn Brown

Aaron Chai

Shailen R. Parmar

Lauren Cook

Steven Goren

Maddie Amick

Alex Johnson

Katie Spencer

Eric Koester

Danny DiMillo

…And everyone else who helped out with *Growing Up in the Grassroots.*

Thank you for making this book possible!

Joy

Made in United States
Orlando, FL
07 September 2022

22145033R00163